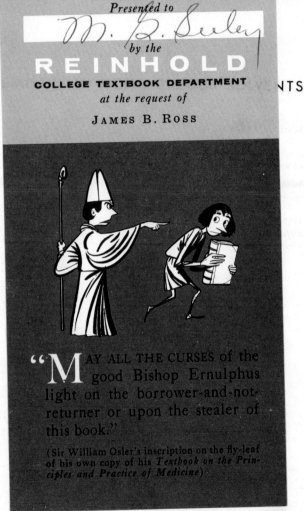

"**M**AY ALL THE CURSES of the good Bishop Ernulphus light on the borrower-and-not-returner or upon the stealer of this book."

(Sir William Osler's inscription on the fly-leaf of his own copy of his *Textbook on the Principles and Practice of Medicine*)

Selected Topics In Modern Chemistry

SERIES EDITORS:

Professor Harry H. Sisler
Department of Chemistry
University of Florida

Professor Calvin A. VanderWerf
Department of Chemistry
University of Kansas

CHEMISTRY IN NON-AQUEOUS SOLVENTS

HARRY H. SISLER

Head Professor of Chemistry
University of Florida

New York
REINHOLD PUBLISHING CORPORATION
Chapman & Hall, Ltd., London

PREFACE

The new series *Selected Topics in Modern Chemistry* is being presented to provide chemistry teachers with supplementary textual materials in order to enrich the undergraduate chemistry curriculum, to enable the teacher to go beyond the textbook in certain important areas, to provide material to challenge the abler student, and, in the case of honors courses, to enable the teacher to assemble a "made-to-order" textbook for his course. The consideration of chemical reactions in solvents other than water is an appropriate and timely topic for one volume of this series.

The solution chemistry of a half-century or so ago was in large measure concerned with reactions which were, or could be, carried out in aqueous solution. Studies of a variety of non-aqueous solvents during the past five decades have, however, resulted in the development of many new solvent systems. The experience thus obtained has greatly broadened the scope of synthetic chemistry and has considerably increased the number and types of theoretical studies which may be carried out.

This book is intended to present to the undergraduate chemistry student some of the basic concepts which relate the chemical and physical characteristics of a solvent to the chemical processes which may be carried out in that solvent, and which determine the usefulness of a given liquid as a solvent. The number of non-aqueous solvents which have been studied during the past half-century is so great that even a cursory treatment of each is impossible in a book of this size. The author has, therefore, chosen deliberately to treat only a few model solvents, viz., liquid ammonia, 100% sulfuric acid, liquid dinitrogen tetroxide, and liquid sulfur dioxide, but to consider them in some detail. These solvents were selected to illustrate the basic principles involved as well as to illustrate some of the principal solvent types.

Throughout the text an effort has been made to show the relationship between the descriptive chemistry presented and the fundamental concepts which the student has learned in his undergraduate chemistry courses. The structure of the solvent molecule and the state of molecular aggregation as well as the various dissociation equilibria in the liquid solvent are emphasized throughout.

The author would like to express his gratitude to two of his former professors: Professor W. Conrad Fernelius, under whom the author received his introduction to the science of chemistry; and Professor L. F. Audrieth, under whose guidance the author carried on his first research in the chemistry of liquid ammonia solutions. If this book is useful in broadening the field of chemical vision of the student and inspiring him to further studies, much of the credit belongs to these two fine chemists and teachers, who have themselves contributed so much to the field of non-aqueous solvent chemistry and who have that rare quality of inspiring and stimulating their students.

The thanks of the author are expressed to Mrs. Bliss Endsley who assisted in the preparation of this manuscript and to Mr. Robert Beach who did the drawings for the illustrations in this book.

HARRY H. SISLER

October, 1961
Gainesville, Florida

CONTENTS

chapter one ————————————————

THE ROLE OF THE SOLVENT
IN CHEMICAL REACTIONS

MOST OF THE reactions carried out by chemists in their researches and in industrial processes and, in fact, a vast majority of those observed in nature occur in solution. The molecules, atoms, or ions of the various reactants are often completely or partially dispersed in some, usually liquid but sometimes solid or gaseous, substance which serves as the medium for the reaction. Because chemists are so accustomed to the presence of a solvent in the reactions they study, they have frequently ignored or, at least insufficiently considered, the effects of the solvent on the course of reactions. This tendency has been particularly unfortunate, since up to the turn of the century chemists were concerned chiefly with reactions in which water—certainly a very distinctive and unusual solvent—served as the solvent medium.

It is, in fact, true that the influence of the solvent on the course of a chemical reaction can be profound, indeed. By changing the solvent, the products from a given set of reactants can be completely changed, and in some cases, reactions may be reversed. For example, in aqueous solution silver nitrate and barium chloride react to form a precipitate of silver chloride leaving barium nitrate in solution, whereas in liquid ammonia solution silver chloride combines with barium nitrate to yield a precipitate of barium chloride, leaving silver nitrate in solution.

Effect of Physical Properties of the Solvent

The range of applicability of various solvents to the carrying out of chemical reactions is determined in no small measure by the physical properties of the solvent.

Melting Point and Boiling Point. Since most reactions in solvent systems are most conveniently carried out in the liquid phase, the temperature range between the melting point and boiling point of the solvent virtually establishes the temperature range of usefulness of the solvent as far as reactions at atmospheric pressure are concerned. This range can be extended by use of a diluent to lower the freezing point and raise the boiling point of the solvent or by operating at increased pressure to raise the boiling point. However, such measures are sufficiently inconvenient to militate considerably against the use of a particular solvent unless some other aspect of the process demands that particular solvent. In the case of liquid ammonia, the abundance and low cost of the solvent combined with its interesting and unusual solvent characteristics cause it to be widely used even though its liquid range at atmospheric pressure ($-77.7°$ C to $-33.35°$ C) is not particularly desirable.

Heat of Fusion and Heat of Vaporization. Since the intermolecular forces in the solid state must be largely overcome when a solid melts, and since intermolecular forces in the liquid phase oppose the vaporization of the liquid it is clear that the magnitudes of the molal heats of fusion and vaporization give us some insight into the nature and strength of the associative forces between molecules in these condensed phases. The degree of chemical association of molecules in a liquid determines to no small extent its solvent properties. Therefore, the heat of fusion and, particularly, the heat of vaporization are significant in evaluating the utility of a solvent.

The ratio of the heat of vaporization to the boiling point on the absolute scale (°K) is a constant called the Trouton constant for many (so-called "normal") liquids, and for these liquids it has the value 21.5. A higher value indicates association of molecules of the liquid to form larger aggregates. Such abnormal liquids include some of our most useful solvents, e.g., water, liquid ammonia, liquid hydrogen fluoride, and the alcohols. One of the most common factors which result in molecular association in the liquid state is polarity of the molecule. Polarity of a molecule results when unsymmetrical molecules contain bonds in which the electron pair forming the bond is shared unequally between the two bonded atoms. Another way of stating this is that polar molecules are molecules in which the center of negative charge (electronic charge) and the center of positive charge (nuclear charge) do not coincide. This is illustrated by the following structures for iodine monochloride and ethyl alcohol.

Association between polar molecules arises from the tendency of polar molecules to orient themselves so that the positive ends of the molecules are near the negative ends of the neighboring molecules as indicated in Fig. 1.1.

One effect of the polarity of a solvent is that polar solutes tend to be much more soluble in liquids of high polarity than they are in non-polar liquids. Where the solute is polar it can enter into association with the molecules of the polar solvents and thus more readily become dispersed in the solvent than would be the case where solvent and solute are strongly different in polarity. Thus, gasoline, composed of virtually non-polar hydrocarbon molecules, is almost completely insoluble

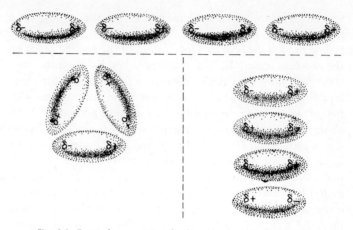

Fig. 1.1. Types of aggregation of polar molecules in the liquid phase.

in the highly polar solvent water, but is completely miscible with the non-polar solvent carbon tetrachloride. On the other hand, the polar substance glucose is highly soluble in water but is virtually insoluble in carbon tetrachloride.

Dielectric Constant. According to Coulomb's well-known law, the force between two charged bodies is given by the expression

$$F = \frac{e_1 e_2}{D r^2}$$

where e_1 and e_2 are the electrical charges on the two bodies, r is the distance between the two charges, and D is a constant called the *dielectric constant* which depends upon the nature of the medium in which the two charged bodies are suspended. It is clear that if D is large the force F will be small. In such a case the medium is said to be an insulating medium. D is usually assigned a value of 1 for a vacuum. Liquids made up of polar molecules (e.g., water and ammonia) usually have very high dielectric constants; for example, the dielectric constant of water at room temperature is about 80.

In order for an ionic solid to dissolve, the electrostatic forces which stabilize the crystal must be greatly reduced. It is clear that this may be accomplished if the ions become suspended in a medium of high dielectric constant. It is, therefore, to be expected that, in general, solvents of high dielectric constant will be much better solvents for ionic substances than are solvents of low dielectric constant. Sodium chloride, an ionic, crystalline substance, dissolves readily in water (Fig. 1.2) but

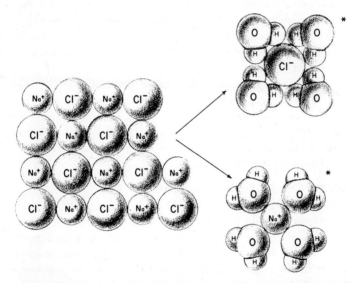

Fig. 1.2. Dissolving of sodium chloride in water. The positive hydrogens of the water molecules are attracted by the Cl^- ions, whereas the negative oxygens are drawn to the Na^+ ions. *The hydrated Na^+ and Cl^- ions probably contain at least six water molecules. Only four are shown for the sake of clarity. (The positive and negative character of the hydrogen and oxygen atoms, respectively, arises from the polar character of the covalent bonds in the water molecule.) (From Sisler, Vanderwerf, and Davidson, "College Chemistry, A Systematic Approach," Macmillan, N. Y., 2nd Edition, 1961.)

is virtually insoluble in the non-polar liquid carbon tetra-chloride.

Viscosity. One of the striking characteristics of various liquids is the differences in their rates of flow. Certain ones such as water, ethyl alcohol, and carbon tetrachloride, are at ordinary temperatures highly fluid and flow rapidly under gravitational force; these are said to be highly mobile. Others such as certain high-molecular weight hydrocarbons and an-hydrous sulfuric acid are highly viscous and flow at much lower rates under a given set of conditions.

Factors affecting viscosity are the temperature of the liquid and the size and shape of the molecule. Generally speaking, lowering the temperature, increasing the molecular size, or making the molecule less symmetrical increases the viscosity of a liquid.

Of particular interest is the fact that increasing the viscosity of a liquid lowers the mobility of ions and molecules in the liquid thus reducing the electrical conductance of solutions of electrolytes in the liquid, and greatly increasing the difficulty of such operations as precipitation, crystallization, and filtra-tion involving that particular liquid.

Effect of Chemical Properties of the Solvent

Of great significance in the selection of solvents for particu-lar chemical applications are the limitations imposed by the chemical nature of the solvent. A reagent used in a given solvent must be one toward which the solvent is either inert, or, at the very least, much less reactive than the substance with which it is supposed to react. Stated in another way, the only reagents available for reaction in a given solvent are those capable of existing for an appropriate period of time in that solvent.

Effect of Acidic or Basic Characteristics of the Solvent. In the discussion which follows it will be assumed that the reader is

aware of the Brønsted-Lowry definitions and the Lewis definitions of acids and bases.* When discussing protonic solvents
we shall use the Brønsted-Lowry definitions and when discussing non-protonic solvents we shall use the somewhat more
general Lewis definitions.

The acidity or basicity of a protonic solvent exerts a most
profound effect on the usefulness of the solvent because of
what is known as the leveling effect of the solvent. This
effect results from the fact that the strongest acid which is
available in a given protonic solvent is that which results from
the self-ionization of the solvent. Likewise, the strongest base
available is that which results from the self-ionization of the
solvent. Consider, for example, the following auto-ionization
reactions:

$$2H_2O \rightleftharpoons H_3O^+ + OH^-$$
$$2NH_3 \rightleftharpoons NH_4^+ + NH_2^-$$
$$2CH_3COOH \rightleftharpoons CH_3C(OH)_2^+ + CH_3COO^-$$

In aqueous solution the strongest acid which can exist and
which, therefore, can be available for reaction is the hydronium ion H_3O^+. All the so-called strong acids familiar to
the chemist appear to have exactly equal strength in aqueous
solution. This results from the fact that these acids, such as
perchloric ($HClO_4$), hydriodic (HI), hydrobromic (HBr),
nitric (HNO_3), and hydrochloric (HCl) all are stronger
proton donors than is the hydronium ion and, hence, all react
completely with water to produce hydronium ion.

$$H:X + H:\overset{..}{\underset{H}{O}}: \rightarrow H:\overset{..}{\underset{H}{O}}:H^+ + :X^-$$

*For a detailed discussion of these concepts see VanderWerf, C. A., "Acids,
Bases, and the Chemistry of the Covalent Bond," Reinhold Publishing Corp.,
New York, 1961.

Thus, acids stronger than H_3O^+ are *leveled* to the strength of H_3O^+ when placed in aqueous solution (Fig. 1.3).

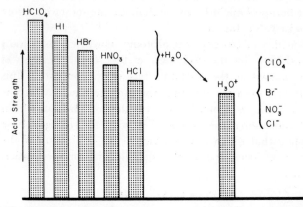

Fig. 1.3. The leveling effect of water on strong acids in aqueous solutions. Relative orders of acidity are not invariable as the solvent or the base is changed. Steric or other factors can cause changes in these orders. A similar statement applies to orders of basicity.

Similarly, the very strong bases such as hydride ion (H^-), amide ion (NH_2^-), and ethoxide ion ($OC_2H_5^-$), all react completely in aqueous solution to yield hydroxide ion (OH^-).

$$X\overset{..}{:}^- + H:\overset{..}{\underset{H}{O}}: \rightarrow H:X + :\overset{..}{\underset{..}{O}}:H^-$$

It is, therefore, fruitless to use such strong bases in aqueous solution for they are immediately leveled to the base strength of hydroxide ion through reaction with the solvent (Fig. 1.4). For example, when sodium hydride, NaH, which contains the very strong base hydride ion (H^-), is added to water a vigorous reaction ensues with the liberation of hydrogen

$$Na^+, \quad :H^- + H:\overset{..}{\underset{H}{O}}: \rightarrow Na^+, \quad :\overset{..}{\underset{..}{O}}:H^- + H:H$$

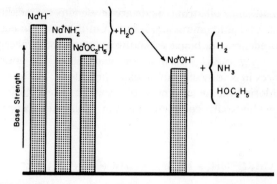

Fig. 1.4. The leveling effect of water on strong bases in aqueous solutions.

and the solution is found to be a solution of sodium hydroxide. Similar reactions ensue when other bases stronger than hydroxide ion are added to water. The reactions with sodium amide and sodium ethoxide are further examples

$$\text{Na}^+, \quad :\!\overset{..}{\underset{H}{N}}\!:\!H^- + H:\overset{..}{\underset{H}{O}}: \longrightarrow \text{Na}^+, \quad :\!\overset{..}{\underset{H}{O}}\!:\!H^- + H:\overset{..}{\underset{H}{N}}:H$$

$$\text{Na}^+, \quad :\!\overset{..}{\underset{..}{O}}\!:\!C_2H_5^- + H:\overset{..}{\underset{H}{O}}: \longrightarrow \text{Na}^+, \quad :\!\overset{..}{\underset{..}{O}}\!:\!H^- + :\!\overset{..}{\underset{H}{O}}:\!C_2H_5$$

It follows, therefore, that the intrinsic acidity and basicity of protonic solvents have a profound effect in determining the usefulness of the solvent in reactions where the availability of highly acidic or basic reagents is important. In the chapters which follow we shall for the various solvents discussed consider examples of such effects.

In terms of the above discussion it is clear that if we wish a solvent in which the intrinsic differences in the proton-donor tendencies of various acids will be evident, we will choose a solvent which has relatively weak proton-acceptor tendencies. Thus, as far as acids are concerned, liquid ammonia is a *level-*

ing solvent, since all strong acids are leveled to the acidity of the weak acid ammonium ion, NH_4^+. On the other hand, anhydrous acetic acid, being a relatively poor proton acceptor, acts as a *differentiating* solvent for acids since the intrinsic differences in acidity of such acids as perchloric, sulfuric, and hydrochloric become evident in this solvent. Perchloric acid undergoes virtually complete reaction with the acetic acid solvent

$$CH_3\overset{\displaystyle O}{\overset{\displaystyle \parallel}{C}}{-}OH + HClO_4 \rightarrow CH_3C(OH)_2^+ + ClO_4^-$$

but sulfuric and hydrochloric acids behave as weak electrolytes in this solvent.

In an analogous manner acetic acid is a leveling solvent toward bases, for anhydrous acetic acid reacts completely with most of the common bases such as CN^-, OH^-, $OC_2H_5^-$, and NH_2^-, leveling all of them to CH_3COO^-. Strongly basic solvents such as liquid ammonia, however, act as differentiating solvents toward bases.

Aprotic solvents, which have neither strong proton-donor tendencies nor strong proton-acceptor tendencies, may act as differentiating solvents for both acids and bases. In such instances the solvent serves principally as the suspending medium for the solute species and itself participates in chemical reactions in the solvent to only a minor extent.

Chemical Effects on Solubility. In addition to the effects already described it should be noted that the solubility of a specific solute in a specific solvent can be greatly increased by chemical interactions between solute and solvent species. For example, acetone is a solvent of very low dielectric constant and the acetone molecule is of low polarity. Yet such protonic solvents as water and ethyl alcohol are miscible with acetone in all proportions. The principal reason for these high solubilities of water and ethyl alcohol in acetone is the interaction of molecules of these compounds with acetone through the mechanism of hydrogen bonding (p. 19).

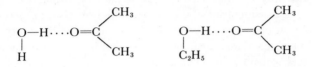

Other examples of this effect include the high solubilities of carbon dioxide and sulfur dioxide in water which result, in part, from their reactions with water to form carbonic and sulfurous acids, respectively.

$$CO_2 + H_2O \rightleftharpoons H_2CO_3$$
$$SO_2 + H_2O \rightleftharpoons H_2SO_3$$

Effects of Oxidizing and Reducing Characteristics. We have seen in the preceding section that the chemistry in a given solvent can be strongly affected by the acidity or basicity of the solvent as well as by chemical effects on solubilities in the solvent. This influence of solvent on the nature of chemical processes which may be carried out in solution in it also extends to the field of oxidation-reduction processes. Water provides an excellent example, for we find that aqueous chemistry does not make available strong reducing agents. The reason for this is that water is so susceptible to reduction (with the release of hydrogen) that strong reducing agents react immediately with water. Hence, only those reducing agents whose electrode potentials are below hydrogen in the electrode potential series are available for aqueous reactions. Another example is provided by liquid ammonia in which strong oxidizing agents may not be used because ammonia is itself a reducing agent and strong oxidizing agents oxidize the ammonia molecules to elementary nitrogen or other oxidation products.

Thus, we see that when the chemist is willing to expand his repertoire of chemical processes and techniques beyond those provided by a single solvent system, he can, through an intelligent consideration of the chemical and physical properties of the various solvents available, greatly broaden the range of chemical reactions which he can run and he can, in many instances, considerably reduce the labor and time involved in achieving a given chemical objective.

Type Reactions in Solvents

Whereas it may readily be shown that virtually all chemical reactions are modified to a degree by the nature of the solvent in which they are carried out, there are certain types of reactions which are more influenced by the nature of the solvent than are others and should at this point, therefore, be briefly noted. Four types of reactions belonging to this category are: (1) precipitation, (2) salt formation, (3) solvolysis, and (4) solvation.

Precipitation. The formation of a precipitate when solutions of two compounds are mixed is one of the most familiar of all chemical processes. Such a manifestation is dependent upon the solubilities of the possible products in the particular solvent as well as upon the various other equilibria involving one or more of the ions composing the product and other components of the solution. Since the values of these solubilities depend in every instance on the nature of the solvent used, it should come as no surprise to find that such precipitation reactions also are highly dependent on the solvent employed. The example of the reversal of the following process

$$BaCl_2 + 2AgNO_3 \rightarrow 2AgCl + Ba(NO_3)_2$$

when the solvent is changed from water to liquid ammonia was given at the beginning of the chapter. Likewise, sodium hydroxide, highly soluble in water, can be precipitated in liquid ammonia; water-soluble ammonium sulfate is virtually insoluble in liquid ammonia, and water-soluble copper sulfate may be precipitated in anhydrous acetic acid.

Salt Formation. If one is seeking to prepare a certain salt, one must bring together an appropriate acid and base, sufficiently acidic and basic, respectively, to react virtually completely with each other. In such an instance, the solvent must be one in which the appropriate acid and base can exist (see p.7). Thus for example, if we wish to prepare the salt $Na^+[H_2N—\overset{\displaystyle O}{\overset{\|}{C}}—NH^-]$, we must use a base capable of taking a proton from the exceedingly weak acid urea. Since the strongest base available in water, viz. the hydroxide ion, will not take a proton from the urea molecule, the salt $Na^+[H_2N—\overset{\displaystyle O}{\overset{\|}{C}}—NH^-]$ may not be prepared in aqueous solution. Viewed another way, the salt is unstable in water and the ureide ion will take a proton from water to form hydroxide ion.

$$Na^+, H_2N—\overset{\displaystyle O}{\overset{\|}{C}}—NH^- + H_2O \rightarrow Na^+, OH^- + H_2N—\overset{\displaystyle O}{\overset{\|}{C}}—NH_2$$

The sodium salt of urea may, however, be readily formed in liquid ammonia solution by the reaction of urea with the strong base sodium amide.

$$H_2N—\overset{\displaystyle O}{\overset{\|}{C}}—NH_2 + Na^+, NH_2^- \rightarrow Na^+, H_2N—\overset{\displaystyle O}{\overset{\|}{C}}—NH^- + NH_3$$

Another interesting example is provided by the salt nitronium perchlorate, $NO_2^+ ClO_4^-$ This salt is formed by the reaction of the very strong acid perchloric acid, $HClO_4$, with the *exceedingly weak base* O_2NOH. (Note that this substance is the well-known strong acid, nitric acid.) This reaction may not be carried out in water, for nitronium ion is incapable of existence in aqueous solution.

$$NO_2^+ + 2H_2O \rightarrow NO_2OH + H_3O^+$$

In the strongly acidic solvent anhydrous sulfuric acid, however, the reaction occurs readily.

$$NO_2OH + HClO_4 \xrightarrow{H_2SO_4} NO_2^+, \ ClO_4^- + H_2O$$

Solvolysis. A solvolytic reaction is a reaction in which the solvent molecule reacts with the solute in such a way that the solvent molecule is split into two parts, one or both of which become attached to a solute molecule or ion. In most instances the solvolytic process results in the development of an increased concentration of either the cation or anion which is characteristic of the autoionization of the solvent. Table 1.1 illustrates this principle:

TABLE 1.1. Solvolytic Reactions

Solvent	Autoionization	Solvolytic Processes
H_2O	$2H_2O \rightleftharpoons H_3O^+ + OH^-$	$SO_2Cl_2 + 4H_2O \rightarrow SO_2(OH)_2 + 2H_3O^+ + 2Cl^-$
		$CN^- + H_2O \rightleftharpoons HCN + OH^-$
NH_3	$2NH_3 \rightleftharpoons NH_4^+ + NH_2^-$	$SO_2Cl_2 + 4NH_3 \rightarrow SO_2(NH_2)_2 + 2NH_4^+ + 2Cl^-$
		$H^- + NH_3 \rightarrow NH_2^- + H_2$
CH_3COOH	$2CH_3COOH \rightleftharpoons CH_3C(OH)_2^+ + CH_3COO^-$	$SO_2Cl_2 + 4CH_3COOH \rightarrow SO_2(OOCCH_3)_2 + 2CH_3C(OH)_2^+ + 2Cl^-$
		$CN^- + CH_3COOH \rightarrow CH_3COO^- + HCN$
C_2H_5OH	$2C_2H_5OH \rightleftharpoons C_2H_5OH_2^+ + OC_2H_5^-$	$SO_2Cl_2 + 4C_2H_5OH \rightarrow SO_2(OC_2H_5)_2 + 2C_2H_5OH_2^+ + 2Cl^-$
		$2CH_3^- + C_2H_5OH \rightarrow OC_2H_5^- + CH_4$

The terms *hydrolysis*, *ammonolysis*, *acetolysis*, and *alcoholysis* are applied to solvolytic reactions in which water, ammonia, acetic acid, and ethyl alcohol are, respectively, the solvents concerned.

Solvation. A solvation reaction is formally a reaction in which a molecule of the solvent attaches itself to a solute species (cation, anion, or molecule) by any of the various types of chemical bonds, notably ion-dipole, hydrogen bonding or coordinate covalent bonding. In certain instances solvation is difficult to distinguish from solvolysis, for the first steps in many solvolytic processes consist of solvation reactions. However, the term solvation is usually applied to those reactions where the solvent molecule remains in the resulting product, though in fact a bond in the solvent molecule may be broken. Some typical examples of solvation reactions are given in Table 1.2.

TABLE 1.2. Examples of Solvate Formation

Solvent	Solvate	Structure (if known)
H_2O	$MgCl_2 \cdot 6H_2O$	$Mg(H_2O)_6{}^{++}$ $2Cl^-$
NH_3	$CuSO_4 \cdot 4NH_3$	$Cu(NH_3)_4{}^{++}$ $SO_4{}^=$
NH_3	$SO_3 \cdot NH_3$	$H^+ : \overset{\displaystyle H : \overset{..}{\underset{..}{O}} :}{\underset{\displaystyle H : \overset{..}{\underset{..}{O}} :}{N : \overset{..}{\underset{..}{S}}{}^- : \overset{..}{\underset{..}{O}} :}}$
CH_3COOH	$K[OOCCH_3] \cdot 2CH_3COOH$	. . . .
H_2SO_4	$BaSO_4 \cdot 3H_2SO_4$	. . . .
N_2O_4	$O(CH_2CH_2)_2O \cdot N_2O_4$	

Solvation of a cation occurs through ion-dipole interaction between the positive cation and the negative end of the solvent dipole or through coordinate covalent bonds in which the solvent molecule shares a pair of electrons with the cation. Solvation of a negative ion can occur through ion-dipole interactions between the negative anion and the positive end of the solvent dipole, or in the case of such solvents as water, ammonia, or hydrogen fluoride, through hydrogen bonding with the anion. In many cases the mechanism of the solvation process and the structure of the resulting solvate is unknown.

Solvation reactions in which water is the solvent are called hydration reactions, and if ammonia is the solvent the reaction is called ammonation. The resulting solvates are known as hydrates and ammoniates, respectively. Other solvates also take their names from the solvent involved, e.g., alcoholates, hydrazinates (from hydrazine) and etherates (from ether).

Summary of the Solvent Characteristics of Water

As a base from which to begin an examination of the chemistries in several non-aqueous solvents, it is useful to summarize briefly the principal characteristics of the solvent water. A list of these characteristics follows:

1. Water freezes at $0°C$ and boils at $100°C$ under one atmosphere pressure and, therefore, has a very convenient liquid temperature range.

2. Water is itself an exceedingly poor electrical conductor, undergoing autoionization according to the equation $2H_2O \rightleftharpoons H_3O^+ + OH^-$ only to an exceedingly small extent.

$$[H_3O^+][OH^-] = 1 \times 10^{-14} \text{ at } 25°C$$

3. The dielectric constant of water at $20°C$ has the very large value 80, and water is, therefore, an excellent solvent for many electrovalent compounds. The resulting solutions are excellent conductors of electricity.

4. Many covalent compounds react with water to give electrically conducting solutions, for the hydration of many covalent compounds results in the production of ions, e.g.

$$HCl + H_2O \rightarrow H_3O^+ + Cl^-$$
$$Al_2Cl_6 + 12H_2O \rightarrow 2Al(H_2O)_6^{+++} + 6Cl^-$$
$$NH_3 + H_2O \rightleftharpoons NH_4^+ + OH^-$$

5. Water is an excellent solvent in which to carry out neutralization reactions, for reactions of this type take place rapidly and smoothly in aqueous solution.

6. Water readily hydrates many salts, acids, and bases through the processes of coordinate covalent bond formation, ion-dipole attraction, or hydrogen-bonding.

7. Reactions involving acids stronger than H_3O^+ ion cannot be carried out in aqueous solution. Likewise, reactions involving bases stronger than OH^- ion may not be carried out in aqueous solution.

8. Reactions involving strong reducing agents may not be carried out in aqueous solution because such reagents would react with water, resulting in the evolution of hydrogen. Moderately strong oxidizing agents may be used in aqueous solution.

9. Because of the labile character of the hydrogen to oxygen bond, hydrolytic reactions proceed rapidly in aqueous solutions. Not only do many salts of weak bases or weak acids undergo hydrolysis but also many acid halides, esters and other covalent substances readily hydrolyze in contact with water.

These then are the characteristics which, along with its abundance, principally account for the wide utilization of water as a solvent. They also indicate important limitations in its usefulness. It will be of interest to compare these characteristics with those of other solvents which we shall consider.

Selected Readings

1. Audrieth, L. F., and Kleinberg, J., "Non-Aqueous Solvents," Chap. 1, John Wiley & Sons, Inc., New York, 1953.
2. Jander, G., "Die Chemie in Wasserähnlichen Lösungsmitteln," Chap. 1, Springer-Verlag, Berlin, 1949.

CHEMISTRY
IN LIQUID AMMONIA

OF THE NUMEROUS non-aqueous solvents now in general use, the earliest to receive systematic investigation as a solvent for chemical reactions was liquid ammonia. Research on liquid ammonia received its first great impetus more than a half-century ago in the studies of E. C. Franklin, C. Kraus, and H. P. Cady at the University of Kansas. Impressed by the similarities of the properties of liquid ammonia and water and also by the correspondence in properties between nitrogen compounds and their isosteric oxygen compound analogues (see p. 26), these three chemists began a series of researches which in the course of the next three decades greatly advanced the understanding and knowledge of nitrogen compounds and placed the use of liquid ammonia as a tool in synthetic chemistry on a very firm footing. Liquid ammonia is now used routinely as the solvent for many types of organic and inorganic syntheses, and as a synthetic reagent in many such processes.

Physical Characteristics of Liquid Ammonia

The principal physical constants for ammonia are listed in Table 2.1.

A comparison of such physical constants for ammonia as

TABLE 2.1. Principal Physical Constants of Ammonia

Melting Point	$-77.74°$ C
Boiling Point	$-33.35°$ C
Heat of Fusion	1352 cal./mole
Heat of Vaporization	5581 cal./mole
Dielectric Constant	26.7 ($-60°$ C)
Heat of Formation (gas)	$-11,040$ cal./mole
Critical Temperature	$133.0°$ C
Critical Pressure	112.3 atm.
Density of Liquid ($-33.4°$ C)	0.677 g./cc.
Specific Conductance ($-35°$ C)	2.94×10^{-7} mho.

melting point, boiling point, heat of vaporization and heat of fusion with the corresponding values for phosphine, arsine, and stibine reveals that the properties of ammonia are abnormal with respect to phosphine, arsine, and stibine in the same sense as the properties of water are out-of-line with respect to hydrogen sulfide, hydrogen selenide, and hydrogen telluride. The properties of hydrogen fluoride are similarly abnormal with respect to the other hydrogen halides. The relationships are illustrated graphically in Fig. 2.1.

The abnormal characteristics of water, ammonia, and hydrogen fluoride are readily explainable on the basis of intermolecular association by means of "hydrogen-bonding." Hydrogen bonds involve the formation of a bridge between two highly electronegative atoms by means of a proton. The nature of this bond is the subject of considerable discussion. Both an electrostatic model and a covalent model for the hydrogen bond have been presented but both of these fail to account for certain experimental observations. Hydrogen bonds are known to have bond energies of the order of a few kilocalories, which is of the right order of magnitude to have a great influence on the properties of solvents.

Ammonia molecules have a high degree of polarity resulting from the pyramidal structure of the molecule and the polarity of the N—H bond. The additional contribution resulting

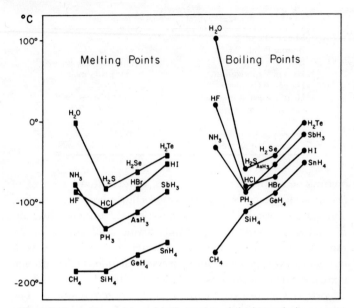

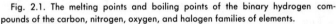

Fig. 2.1. The melting points and boiling points of the binary hydrogen compounds of the carbon, nitrogen, oxygen, and halogen families of elements.

from the configuration of the charge distribution of the unshared electron pair must not, however, be neglected. It is believed that the bonding orbitals used by the nitrogen atom in uniting with three hydrogen atoms are sp^3 hybrids. The fourth orbital would, therefore, be an sp^3 hybrid also and would be directed in space in such a way that the negative charge density of the electron pair occupying that orbital would reinforce the dipole resulting from the three N—H bonds. These relationships are illustrated in Fig. 2.2. The bond angle H—N—H (107°) is somewhat less than tetrahedral because of the "compressive" effect of the repulsion of the bonding electrons by the unshared pair. This repulsion is greater than that between the bonding pairs.

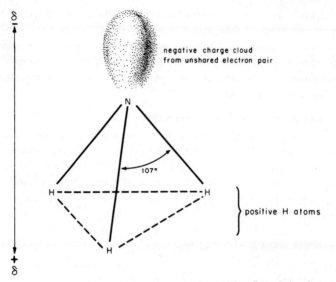

Fig. 2.2. Structure of the ammonia molecule showing the effect of the electron cloud from the unshared electron pair on the polarity of the NH_3 molecule.

In the ammonia crystal each nitrogen atom has six neighboring nitrogen atoms at a distance of 3.380 ± 0.004 Å, this distance corresponding to that of a weak $N—H \cdots N$ bond. The energy of this bond, as estimated from the heat of sublimation of ammonia, and assuming a value of 2600 cal./mole for Van der Waals forces, is approximately 1300 cal./mole.

Liquid ammonia undergoes autoionization in a manner analogous to that of water but, as its very low specific conductance indicates, the extent of autoionization is even less than that of water.

$$2NH_3 \rightleftharpoons NH_4^+ + NH_2^-$$

The ion-product constant, $K_{ion} = [NH_4^+][NH_2^-]$ has been estimated to have the very low value of 1.9×10^{-33} at $-50°$ C.

Liquid ammonia is also characterized by a high degree of mobility even at low temperatures. This means that conductance values for typical electrolytes in liquid ammonia tend to be quite high. It also has an unusually high thermal coefficient of expansion, i.e., its density decreases rapidly with rise in temperature.

Chemical Characteristics of Ammonia

The chemical reactions of ammonia may be divided into three groups: (1) *ammonation* reactions in which the ammonia molecule combines with another molecule, atom, or ion by means of coordinate covalent, ion-dipole, or hydrogen bonds; (2) *ammonolytic* reactions in which an atom, ion, or radical from the compound undergoing ammonolysis is replaced by an amide ($-NH_2$), imide ($=NH$), or nitride ($\equiv N$) group; and (3) *oxidation-reduction* reactions in which the nitrogen or hydrogen atom of the ammonia molecule undergoes a change in oxidation state.

Ammonation. Because of its ability to share a pair of electrons with an electron-acceptor, as well as through the mechanism of ion-dipole attraction, ammonia forms a great many complex compounds. Notable among these are the ammonia complexes with various metal ions. Typical examples include $[Hg(NH_3)_2]^+$, $[Pt(NH_3)_4]^{++}$, $[Cu(NH_3)_4]^{++}$, $[Cr(NH_3)_6]^{+++}$, $[Co(NH_3)_6]^{+++}$, and $[Ni(NH_3)_6]^{++}$. Salts containing these ammonia complexes are called *ammines* and include such compounds a $[Ag(NH_3)_2]Cl$, $[Pt(NH_3)_4]Cl_2$, $[Cu(NH_3)_4]SO_4 \cdot H_2O$, $[Cr(NH_3)_6]Cl_3$, $[Co(NH_3)_6](NO_3)_3$, and $[Ni(NH_3)_6]Br_2$. These ammines are formal analogues of the corresponding aqueous compounds, the salt hydrates, but the two groups of compounds differ in many respects. Ammines are prepared by the ammonation of the metal salts in aqueous solution, in liquid ammonia solution, or by the action of gaseous ammonia on the anhydrous salt.

More familiar among the ammonation reactions, however, is the reaction with water through the mechanism of hydrogen bonding:

$$H:\overset{\displaystyle H}{\underset{\displaystyle H}{N}}: \; + \; H:\overset{..}{\underset{..}{O}}: \; \rightleftharpoons \; H:\overset{\displaystyle H}{N}:H:\overset{..}{\underset{..}{O}}: \; \rightleftharpoons \; H:\overset{\displaystyle H}{\underset{\displaystyle H}{N}}:H^+ \; + \; :\overset{..}{\underset{..}{O}}:H^-$$

The strong tendency for this reaction to occur explains the very high solubility of ammonia in water or of water in liquid ammonia. Phase diagrams for the binary system ammonia-water (Fig. 2.3) indicate the existence of the solid hydrates $NH_3 \cdot H_2O$ and $2NH_3 \cdot H_2O$ at temperatures below about $-80°$ C. Infrared spectral data* on these crystals indicate the

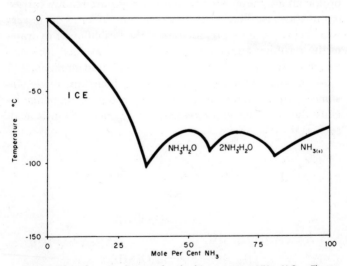

Fig. 2.3. Freezing point diagram for the binary system NH_3—H_2O. The two maxima in the curve indicate the formation of the compounds $NH_3 \cdot H_2O$ and $2NH_3 \cdot H_2O$.

*Waldron, R. D., and Hornig, D. F., *J. Am. Chem. Soc.*, **75**, 6079 (1953).

absence of ions in the crystal lattices, and, in the hydrate $2NH_3 \cdot H_2O$, the two ammonia molecules appear to be non-equivalent. The hydrates of ammonia are weak electrolytes in aqueous solution as evidenced by the value of 1.65×10^{-5} at $25°C$ for the ionization constant $[NH_4^+][OH^-]/[NH_3 \cdot aq]$.

Because of the strongly basic character of the ammonia molecules, ammonation reactions with a variety of hydrogen acids take place in accordance with the general equation:

$$\begin{matrix} H && H \\ \overset{..}{\underset{..}{H:N:}} + H:X \rightarrow & \overset{..}{\underset{..}{H:N:}}H^+ + :X^- \\ H && H \end{matrix}$$

As we shall see (pp. 40, 41), if the acid is a sufficiently strong proton donor, these ammonation reactions are readily carried out in aqueous solution. If, however, ammonium salts of very weak acids are to be prepared, or if the formation of hydrates of the resulting ammonium salts is to be avoided, the ammonation reactions may be carried out in liquid ammonia.

Additional ammonation reactions which, in many instances, are conveniently carried out in liquid ammonia include the formation of ammoniates of a variety of Lewis acids such as the following:

$$SO_3 + 2NH_3 \rightarrow SO_2 \overset{\displaystyle O[NH_4]}{\underset{\displaystyle NH_2}{\big\langle}} \qquad (SO_3 \cdot 2NH_3)$$

$$2SO_3 + 4NH_3 \rightarrow [H_4N]N \overset{\displaystyle SO_2O[NH_4]}{\underset{\displaystyle SO_2O[NH_4]}{\big\langle}} \qquad (2SO_3 \cdot 4NH_3)$$

$$SiF_4 + 2NH_3 \rightarrow SiF_4 \cdot 2NH_3$$

$$BF_3 + NH_3 \rightarrow BF_3 \cdot NH_3$$

Ammonolysis. Ammonia undergoes numerous reactions which result in the substitution of an atom, ion, or radical from the substance with which the ammonia is reacting by a nitrogen-containing ion or radical. Examples of such ammonolytic reactions include the following:

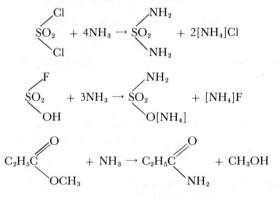

$$C_6H_5Cl + 2NH_3 \rightarrow C_6H_5NH_2 + [NH_4]Cl$$

Though the ammonia molecule is basic and has a strong tendency to accept protons, it will, toward very strong bases, act as a proton donor. Examples of this type of ammonolysis include:

$$Na^+, H^- + NH_3 \rightarrow Na^+, NH_2^- + H_2$$

$$Na^+, CH_3^- + NH_3 \rightarrow Na^+, NH_2^- + CH_4$$

In many instances, these reactions are most conveniently carried out in liquid ammonia.

Oxidation-Reduction. Examples of reactions in which ammonia acts as a reducing agent include the catalytic oxidation of ammonia to nitric oxide

$$4NH_3 + 5O_2 \xrightarrow{Pt} 4NO + 6H_2O$$

and the reduction of metal oxides with ammonia at high temperatures

$$3CuO + 2NH_3 \xrightarrow{\Delta} 3Cu + 3H_2O + N_2$$

In its reactions with active metals, ammonia acts as an oxidizing agent:

$$2Na + 2NH_3 \rightarrow 2NaNH_2 + H_2$$

$$3Mg + 2NH_3 \rightarrow Mg_3N_2 + 3H_2$$

Ammonia is oxidized by some non-metals, e.g., chlorine oxidizes ammonia to chloramine in the gas phase, in aqueous solution, or in liquid ammonia.

$$Cl_2 + 2NH_3 \rightarrow NH_2Cl + NH_4Cl$$

Furthermore, it is worth noting that if the ammonia is not in excess, dichloramine ($NHCl_2$), nitrogen trichloride (NCl_3), or nitrogen are formed.

The Nitrogen System of Compounds

One of the fruits of early investigation of reactions in liquid ammonia was the recognition by E. C. Franklin that just as many of the familiar oxygen compounds may be thought of as being derived from water as *parent solvent*, so also may a great variety of nitrogen compounds be considered as belonging to a *nitrogen or ammonia system of compounds* for which ammonia is the parent solvent. This analogy has proved most useful in understanding the chemistry of nitrogen compounds for it has been observed that the reactions of many nitrogen compounds in liquid ammonia solution are analogous to the reactions of their oxygen analogues in aqueous solution.

Formulas for the nitrogen analogues of the various oxygen compounds can be formally derived by replacing oxygen-containing radicals by their nitrogen-containing isosteres.* Corresponding nitrogen- and oxygen-containing isosteres are given in Table 2.2. This relationship is illustrated by a series of analogues in the water (aquo) and ammonia (ammono)

---

*Isosteres are groups containing the same number of electrons and the same number of nuclear charges.

TABLE 2.2. Isosteric Groups in the Oxygen and Nitrogen Systems

Nitrogen-Containing	NH_4^+	NH_3	NH_2^-	NH^-	$N^{\equiv}$
Oxygen-Containing	H_3O^+	H_2O	OH^-	$O^=$	. . . .

systems listed in Table 2.3. Compounds in which both oxygen-containing and nitrogen-containing groups are present are considered as belonging to both systems, i.e., are called aquo-ammono compounds.

A series of analogous reactions in the aqueous and ammonia systems are listed in Table 2.4.

The correlation of properties between aquo and ammono acids, aquo and ammono bases, and other corresponding aquo and ammono series has proved most fruitful. However, one should remember that this series of analogies, like most other analogies, is not perfect, and is, therefore, suggestive rather than definitive in its application to the study of chemistry in non-aqueous solvents. In our discussions of reactions in liquid ammonia we shall consider a number of examples of the useful application of this type of correlation.

Solubilities in Liquid Ammonia

It may, in general, be remarked that, as might be expected from the fact that its dielectric constant is much less than that of water, liquid ammonia is a much better solvent for organic compounds than is water. On the other hand, liquid ammonia is, in general, a poorer solvent for ionic substances than is water. There are, however, many ionic compounds which have a high degree of solubility in liquid ammonia.

Elements. Among the metallic elements, the alkali metals and alkaline earth metals are highly soluble in liquid ammonia, giving characteristic blue colored solutions. Europium and ytterbium, and possibly other rare earth metals, likewise form these solutions. Under special conditions liquid ammonia solutions of aluminum and beryllium are obtainable. These metal-ammonia solutions will be discussed in detail in a later section (p. 31).

The non-metals phosphorus, sulfur, and iodine, dissolve readily in liquid ammonia, but these solubility processes involve reaction with the solvent.   For example, the solution

TABLE 2.3   Analogous Aquo, Aquo-Ammono, and Ammono Compounds

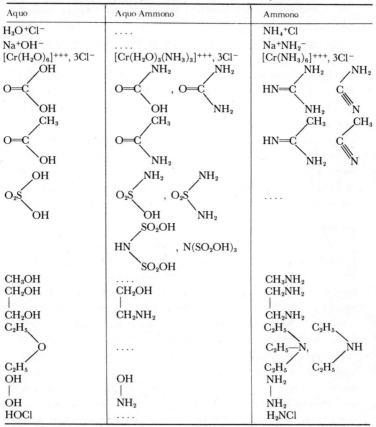

Aquo	Aquo Ammono	Ammono
$H_3O^+Cl^-$	....	NH_4^+Cl
Na^+OH^-	....	$Na^+NH_2^-$
$[Cr(H_2O)_6]^{+++}, 3Cl^-$	$[Cr(H_2O)_3(NH_3)_3]^{+++}, 3Cl^-$	$[Cr(NH_3)_6]^{+++}, 3Cl^-$

TABLE 2.4. Corresponding Reactions in the Water and Ammonia Systems

Aquo	Ammonia
$H_3O^+, Cl^- + Na^+, OH^- \rightarrow 2H_2O + Na^+, Cl^-$	$NH_4^+, Cl^- + Na^+, NH_2^- \rightarrow 2NH_3 + Na^+, Cl^-$
$Zn + 2H_3O^+ \rightarrow Zn^{++} + H_2 + 2H_2O$	$Zn + 2NH_4^+ \rightarrow Zn^{++} + H_2 + 2NH_3$
$CH_3C(=O)(OC_2H_5) + H_2O \xrightarrow{H_3O^+} CH_3C(=O)(OH) + C_2H_5OH$	$CH_3C(=NH)(NHC_2H_5) + NH_3 \xrightarrow{NH_4^+} CH_3C(=NH)(NH_2) + C_2H_5NH_2$
$O{=}C(OH)(OH) + 2OH^- \rightarrow O{=}C(O^-)(O^-) + 2H_2O$	$HN{=}C(NH_2)(NH_2) + 2NH_2^- \rightarrow HN{=}C(NH^-)(NH^-) + 2NH_3$
$Zn(OH)_2 + 2OH^- \rightarrow Zn(OH)_4^{--}$	$Zn(NH_2)_2 + 2NH_2^- \rightarrow Zn(NH_2)_4^=$
$Cu^{++}SO_4^= + 5H_2O \rightarrow Cu(H_2O)_4^{++}SO_4 \cdot H_2O^=$	$Cu^{++}SO_4^= + 4NH_3 \rightarrow Cu(NH_3)_4^{++}, SO_4^=$
$Na_3As + 3H_3O^+, Br^- \rightarrow AsH_3 + 3Na^+, Br^- + 3H_2O$	$Na_3As + 3NH_4^+, Br^- \rightarrow AsH_3 + 3Na^+, Br^- + 3NH_3$

process for sulfur has been shown to be

$$5/4S_8 + 16NH_3 \rightleftharpoons N_4S_4 + 6(NH_4)_2S$$

As indicated, this reaction is reversible and the evaporation of a freshly prepared liquid ammonia solution of sulfur yields free sulfur again.

Inorganic Compounds. There are few, if any, salts of multivalent anions which have appreciable solubility in liquid ammonia. Thus, sulfates, sulfites, carbonates, phosphates, arsenates, oxides, and sulfides, are virtually insoluble in liquid ammonia. Metal hydroxides are likewise insoluble. All the metal amides except those of the alkali metals are insoluble. Lithium amide is also insoluble, and sodium amide is soluble only to the extent of 0.004 g. per 100 g. of NH_3. Potassium, rubidium, and cesium amides have a considerable solubility in liquid ammonia.

The metal salts which are, in general, most soluble in liquid ammonia include the thiocyanates, perchlorates, nitrates, nitrites, and many of the iodides. It is particularly interesting to note that in liquid ammonia the general order of solubility for halides is as follows: iodides > bromides > chlorides > fluorides. Most ammonium salts (except those of multivalent anions as mentioned above) are soluble in liquid ammonia, and some of these, such as the nitrate, acetate, and thiocyanate, are so highly soluble as to cause them to deliquesce in the presence of ammonia gas. Saturated solutions of these ammono-deliquescent salts have such a low vapor pressure of ammonia as to be stable at $0°C$. A saturated solution of ammonium nitrate in liquid ammonia is stable at room temperature.

The solubilities of several inorganic salts in liquid ammonia at $25°C$ are listed in Table 2.5.

Data on the solubilities of various metal halides in liquid ammonia at $0°C$ are listed in Table 2.6.

TABLE 2.5.* Solubilities in Liquid Ammonia at 25° C. (g./100 g. NH_3)

NH_4Cl	102.5	KNH_2	3.6
NH_4Br	237.9	KCl	0.04
NH_4I	368.4	KBr	13.5
NH_4SCN	312.0	KI	182.0
NH_4ClO_4	137.9	$KCNO$	1.70
NH_4NO_3	390.0	$KClO_3$	2.52
$(NH_4)_2S$	120.0	$KBrO_3$	0.002
$(NH_4)_2SO_3$	0.0	KI_3	0.0
$(NH_4)_2HPO_4$	0.0	KNO_3	10.4
$(NH_4)HCO_3$	0.0	K_2SO_4	0.0
$(NH_4)_2CO_3$	0.0	K_2CO_3	0.0
$(NH_4)(CH_3COO)$	253.2		
		$AgCl$	0.83
$LiNO_3$	243.66	$AgBr$	5.92
Li_2SO_4	0.0	AgI	206.84
		$AgNO_3$	86.04
$NaNH_2$	0.004		
NaF	0.35	$Ca(NO_3)_2$	80.22
$NaCl$	3.02	$Sr(NO_3)_2$	87.08
$NaBr$	137.95	$Ba(NO_3)_2$	97.22
NaI	161.9	$BaCl_2$	0.0
$NaSCN$	205.5		
$NaNO_3$	97.6	MnI_2	0.02
$Na_2S_2O_3$	0.17	ZnI_2	0.1
Na_2SO_4	0.0	ZnO	0.0
		H_3BO_3	1.92

*Jander, G., "Die Chemie in Wasserahnliehen Lösungsmitteln," Springer-Verlag, Berlin, p. 48, 1949.

Organic Compounds. In general, the solubilities of organic compounds in liquid ammonia are considerably higher than the corresponding solubilities in water. Pertinent information is summarized in Table 2.7.

Solutions of Alkali Metals in Liquid Ammonia

There are few phenomena in the chemistry of non-aqueous solvents which through the years have so fascinated chemists as has the dissolution of active metals (alkali metals, alkaline earth metals, aluminum and some rare earth metals) in liquid ammonia. Metals having low ionization potentials, low sub-limation energies, and high energies of solvation, i.e., metals having very high electrode potentials, readily dissolve in liquid ammonia to give blue colored solutions which, when dilute, have identical absorption spectra regardless of which metal is the solute in the particular solution. The solutions are ex-tremely good electrolytic conductors and, at all concentra-tions, the equivalent conductances obtained for the various metal-ammonia solutions are greater than those known for

TABLE 2.6.* Solubilities of Metal Halides in Liquid Ammonia at 0° C. (g./100 g. soln.)

Cation	Anion			
	Cl⁻	Br⁻	I⁻	NO₃⁻
Li^+	1.43	. . .	. . .	. . .
Na^+	11.37	39.00	56.88	56.05
K^+	0.132	21.18	64.81	9.52
Rb^+	0.289	18.23	68.15	. . .
Cs^+	0.381	4.38	60.28	. . .
Ag^+	0.280	2.35	84.15	. . .
NH_4^+	39.91	57.96	76.99	. . .
Mg^{++}	. . .	0.004	0.156	. . .
Ca^{++}	. . .	0.009	3.85	45.13
Sr^{++}	. . .	0.008	0.308	28.77
Ba^{++}	. . .	0.017	0.231	17.88

*Linhard and Stephan, *Z. physik. Chem.*, **A163**, 185 (1933); **A167**, 87 (1933).

any other electrolyte in any known solvent. Highly con-centrated solutions ($>1\ M$) are bronze in color and approach "metallic-type" electrical conductance. Instead of a highly positive thermal coefficient of conductance as is characteristic of electrolytic conductors, these solutions have thermal co-efficients only slightly greater than zero. The thermal coef-ficient of electrical conductance for sodium or potassium solu-tions increases with increasing concentrations of the metal and after passing through a maximum decreases to very

TABLE 2.7.   Solubilities of Organic Compounds in Liquid Ammonia

Hydrocarbons: Alkanes are insoluble. Alkenes and Alkynes have a slight solubility. Benzene is highly soluble. Toluene forms two liquid layers with liquid ammonia below 15° C.

Alcohols: Polyhydric alcohols and simple alcohols are miscible with liquid ammonia in all proportions. Hydroxy benzenes (phenol, etc.) are quite soluble.

Carboxylic Acids: Converted to ammonium salts. Those of low molecular weight acids are soluble. Solubility is less for the higher molecular-weight compounds.

Esters: Simple esters are highly soluble in liquid ammonia, but as the alkyl groups increase in size, solubility decreases.

Aldehydes and Ketones: Moderately soluble but aldehydes and some ketones react with ammonia.

Ethers: Diethyl ether is moderately soluble but higher molecular-weight ethers are less so.

Alkyl Sulfuric and Alkyl and Aryl Sulfonic Acids: Converted to ammonium salts which are soluble in liquid ammonia.

Amines: Simple amines are quite soluble in liquid ammonia but solubility decreases with increasing molecular weight. Primary amines are more soluble than secondary amines which are more soluble than tertiary amines.

Acid Amides and Amidines: Simple members of these series are quite soluble.

Heterocyclic Nitrogen Bases: Pyridine, quinoline, indole, pyrrole, carbazole, simple triazoles, and simple tetrazoles are quite soluble in liquid ammonia.

nearly zero for saturated solutions. (Fig. 2.4). Normal metals have a negative thermal coefficient of conductance. All of these metal-ammonia solutions are metastable and upon long standing, or in the presence of a suitable catalyst, undergo decomposition to yield hydrogen gas and the amide.

$$M + nNH_3 \rightarrow n/2H_2 + M(NH_2)_n$$

This decomposition process is, however, exceedingly slow in clean apparatus if pure reagents are used and the solutions are kept cold.

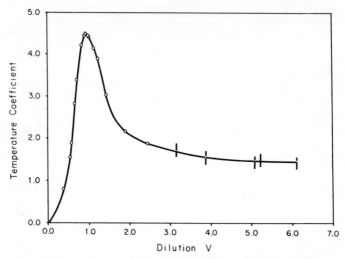

Fig. 2.4. Temperature coefficient of electrical conductivity for potassium-ammonia solutions as a function of dilution. (Drawn from results of Kraus and Lucasse, *J. Am. Chem. Soc.,* **45**, 2551 (1923).)

Ammonia solutions of aluminum and beryllium are relatively less stable than alkali or alkaline earth metal solutions and are formed by the cathodic reduction of ammonia solutions of aluminum iodide and beryllium chloride, respectively. Blue solutions of tetralkylammonium radicals, $R_4N \cdot$, in liquid ammonia are prepared by cathodic reduction of tetralkylammonium halide solutions.

The solubilities of some of the alkali metals in liquid ammonia at various temperatures are given in Table 2.8.

When solutions of alkali metals in liquid ammonia are evaporated, the free metal is recovered. However, when ammonia solutions of calcium, barium, or strontium are evaporated solid phases having the approximate compositions $Ca(NH_3)_6$, $Sr(NH_3)_6$, and $Ba(NH_3)_6$, are obtained. These phases are excellent electrical conductors and are metallic in appearance. Under reduced pressure ammonia can be re-

TABLE 2.8. Solubilities of Li, Na, K, and Cs in Liquid NH_3

Lithium							
Temp., °C	− 0	−33.2	−39.4	− 63.5	. . .	. . .	. . . .
Molality	16.31	15.66	16.25	15.41	. . .	. . .	. . .
Sodium							
Temp., °C	22	0	−30	− 33.5		−70	−100
Molality	9.56	10.00	10.63	10.93		11.29	11.79
Potassium							
Temp., °C	0	−33.2	−50	−100	−33.5	. . .	. . .
Molality	12.4	11.86	12.3	12.2	12.05	. . .	. . .
Cesium							
Temp., °C	−50	. . .	. . .	. . .	. . .	. . .	. . .
Molality	25.1	. . .	. . .	. . .	. . .	. . .	. . .

moved from these metal-ammine phases leaving the free metal, but this process is usually accompanied by some decomposition to metal amide plus hydrogen.

An interesting aspect of several metal-ammonia systems is the fact that in certain temperature and concentration ranges the systems exist as two immiscible liquid phases in equilibrium. The heavier of these phases is blue and is the less concentrated in the metal; the lighter phase is the more concentrated in the metal and is bronze in color. This behavior has been reported for the lithium, sodium, potassium, calcium, strontium, and barium systems. The phase diagram for the sodium-ammonia system has been partially worked out and is shown in Fig. 2.5.

Dilute solutions of metals in liquid ammonia are paramagnetic, i.e., are attracted into a magnetic field. In a system of this type this is an indication of the existence of unpaired electrons. However, as the concentration of the metal in the ammonia solution increases, the molar magnetic susceptibility decreases, indicating that the fraction of the electrons which are unpaired decreases with increasing concentrations of the metal.

On the basis of observations of the physical properties of various metal-ammonia solutions we may qualitatively describe these solutions as follows:

In highly dilute solutions (electrolytic solutions) the metal atoms are essentially ionized into ammoniated metal ions and ammoniated electrons.

$$M \rightarrow M^+_{(am)} + e^-_{(am)}$$

The electrons occupy cavities surrounded by ammonia molecules whose protons are oriented toward the free electrons. As

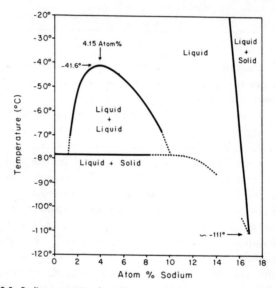

Fig. 2.5. Sodium-ammonia phase diagram. (Redrawn by permission from Cotton (ed.), "Progress in Inorganic Chemistry," Vol. 1, Interscience, N. Y., 1959.)

the concentration increases, the ammoniated metal ions tend to bond together by electrons into aggregates such as M_2, M_3, etc. In concentrated solutions (metallic) the ammoniated metal ions are bonded by the electrons in a manner analogous to that of ordinary metal ions of the same size in a molten metal.

Reactions in Liquid Ammonia

In our brief survey of reactions for which liquid ammonia is appropriately used as solvent, we shall find it convenient to divide these reactions into five types: (1) metatheses depending upon solubility relationships; (2) reactions of ammono acids; (3) reactions of ammono bases; (4) reactions of metal-ammonia solutions; and (5) ammonolyses.

Metatheses. Because of differences in solubilities of various substances in liquid ammonia and in water, numerous metatheses which do not occur in water may be conveniently carried out in liquid ammonia. We have already mentioned the precipitation of barium chloride from solutions of silver chloride and barium nitrate in liquid ammonia. There are numerous other such reactions, for example, the precipitation of sodium carbamate by the reaction:

$$NH_4[O{=}CNH_2] + NaNO_3 \rightarrow Na[O{-}C{=}O{-}NH_2] + NH_4NO_3$$

the precipitation of metal alcoholates by the reactions of the proper metal salt with potassium alcoholate in liquid ammonia

$$2K[OR] + Me^{++} \rightarrow Me[OR]_2 + 2K^+$$

the precipitation of lithium chloride from liquid ammonia solutions of ammonium chloride and lithium nitrate

$$[NH_4]Cl + LiNO_3 \rightarrow LiCl + [NH_4]NO_3$$

and the precipitation of barium sulfide from ammonia solutions of barium nitrate

$$Ba[NO_3]_2 + [NH_4]_2S \rightarrow BaS_{(am)} + 2[NH_4]NO_3$$

Reactions of Ammono Acids. Ammonium salts are all acidic. They are the ammono analogues of hydronium ions in the aqueous system. The ammono analogues of metal hydroxides are the metal amides. A typical neutralization reaction is the reaction of ammonium chloride with potassium amide:

$$[NH_4]Br + KNH_2 \rightarrow KBr + 2NH_3$$

or written ionically:

$$NH_4^+ + NH_2^- \rightarrow 2NH_3$$

It should be remembered that because of the leveling effect of the basic ammonia solvent, the strongest acid available in liquid ammonia is the ammonium ion. Ammonia is not a suitable solvent, therefore, for reactions requiring strong acids.

Liquid ammonia solutions of ammonium salts react with active metals to yield hydrogen, e.g., blue solutions of alkali metals in liquid ammonia are decolorized by ammonium salts:

$$Na + NH_4^+ \rightarrow Na^+ + \tfrac{1}{2}H_2 + NH_3$$

Other examples of the many metal-ammonium ion reactions include the solution of manganese in solutions of ammonium bromide or nitrate, cobalt and nickel in ammonium nitrate solution, iron in ammonium cyanide solution, and lanthanum and cerium in ammonium iodide solution.

Ammonium salts dissolved in liquid ammonia also serve as acids in the synthesis of various hydrides. Thus, the reactions of magnesium silicide and magnesium germanide with liquid ammonia solutions of ammonium bromide give high yields of the lower silanes and germanes, respectively.

$$Mg_nSi_m \xrightarrow[NH_3]{NH_4Br} SiH_4 \text{ in high yields}$$

$$Mg_nGe_m \xrightarrow[NH_3]{NH_4Br} GeH_4 \text{ in high yields.}$$

Ammono acids undergo protolysis in liquid ammonia. As a matter of fact, certain compounds whose proton donor characteristics are so weak that they do not donate protons to water readily undergo protolysis in liquid ammonia. Thus,

guanidine $(NH_2\overset{\displaystyle \parallel^{NH}}{C}-NH_2)$ and urea $(NH_2\overset{\displaystyle \parallel^{O}}{C}-NH_2)$, both of
which actually behave as proton acceptors in water, donate
protons to ammonia molecules in liquid ammonia. Similarly,
sulfamic acid which is a strong monobasic acid toward the
bases available in aqueous solution

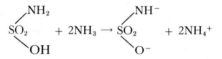

$$SO_2\begin{smallmatrix}\diagup NH_2 \\ \diagdown OH\end{smallmatrix} + H_2O \rightarrow SO_2\begin{smallmatrix}\diagup NH_2 \\ \diagdown O^-\end{smallmatrix} + H_3O^+$$

behaves as a dibasic acid towards the more strongly basic ammonia or the stronger bases available in liquid ammonia as a
solvent.

$$SO_2\begin{smallmatrix}\diagup NH_2 \\ \diagdown OH\end{smallmatrix} + 2NH_3 \rightarrow SO_2\begin{smallmatrix}\diagup NH^- \\ \diagdown O^-\end{smallmatrix} + 2NH_4^+$$

Likewise, sulfamide, $(NH_2SO_2NH_2)$ which does not donate
protons to water, transfers protons to ammonia molecules.

Acetamidine $(CH_3\overset{\displaystyle \parallel^{NH}}{C}-NH_2)$, i.e., ammono acetic acid, and

acetamide $(CH_3\overset{\displaystyle \parallel^{O}}{C}-NH_2)$, i.e., aquo ammono acetic acid, are
too weak as acids to yield protons in aqueous solutions. Both
of these compounds, however, transfer protons to ammonia.

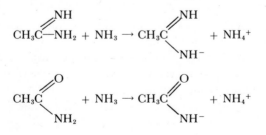

$$CH_3\overset{\displaystyle \parallel^{NH}}{C}-NH_2 + NH_3 \rightarrow CH_3\overset{\displaystyle \parallel^{NH}}{C}\begin{smallmatrix} \\ \diagdown NH^-\end{smallmatrix} + NH_4^+$$

$$CH_3\overset{\displaystyle \diagup^{O}}{C}\begin{smallmatrix} \\ \diagdown NH_2\end{smallmatrix} + NH_3 \rightarrow CH_3\overset{\displaystyle \diagup^{O}}{C}\begin{smallmatrix} \\ \diagdown NH^-\end{smallmatrix} + NH_4^+$$

Salts of these ammono and aquo ammono acids are readily prepared by their reaction with liquid ammonia solutions of the very strong base potassium amide, e.g.,

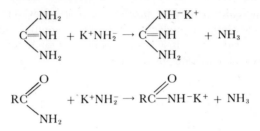

Reactions of Ammono Bases. The most familiar reactions in liquid ammonia involving ammono bases are reactions of ammonia solutions of the amide ion, NH_2^-. Because of the very small solubilities of lithium amide and sodium amide, as well as of the amides of the alkaline earth metals, the most convenient ammono base to use in liquid ammonia is potassium amide.

Reactions of such solutions with metal ions in liquid ammonia result in the precipitation of metal amides, imides, or nitrides (analogous to the precipitation of metal hydroxides and oxides in aqueous systems).

$$
\left.\begin{array}{l} AgNO_3 \\ PbI_2 \\ HgI_2 \\ BiI_3 \\ TlNO_3 \end{array}\right\} \xrightarrow[NH_{3(l)}]{K^+ \ NH_2^-} \left\{\begin{array}{l} AgNH_2 \\ PbNH \\ Hg_3N_2 \\ BiN \\ Tl_3N \end{array}\right.
$$

Such reactions provide the only presently known means for preparing nitrides of the very noble metals. Many of these imide or nitride derivatives of the less active metals (e.g., the nitrides of thallium, bismuth, and mercury) are explosive and should be treated with care.

It is well known that hydroxides (or oxides) of certain metals dissolve in an excess of an aqueous solution of hydroxide ion (e.g., aqueous NaOH solution) to yield hydroxo complexes of the corresponding metal ions, e.g.,

$$Zn(OH)_2 + 2Na^+, OH^- \rightarrow 2Na^+, Zn(OH)_4^{--}$$

Many metal amides, imides, and nitrides are similarly dissolved in solutions of potassium amide in liquid ammonia; in fact, because of the very strongly basic character of the amide ion, the formation of amido complexes occurs for more metal ions than is true of hydroxo complexes. The following examples are illustrative:

$$
\left.
\begin{array}{l}
AgNH_2 \\
BeNH \\
Zn(NH_2)_2 \\
PbNH \\
Al(NH)(NH_2) \\
NaNH_2
\end{array}
\right\}
\xrightarrow[NH_{3(l)}]{K^+, \ NH_2^-}
\begin{array}{l}
K[Ag(NH_2)_2] \\
K[Be(NH_2)_3] \\
K_2[Zn(NH_2)_4] \\
K[Pb(NH)(NH_2)] \\
K[Al(NH_2)_4] \\
K_2[Na(NH_2)_3]
\end{array}
$$

Thus, even sodium amide is soluble in a liquid ammonia solution of potassium amide.

Since amide ion is a much stronger base than is hydroxide ion, liquid ammonia makes available more strongly basic reagents than does water. Hence, many reactions requiring very strong bases are conveniently carried out in liquid ammonia. Among these are the formation of salts of very weak acids (e.g., guanidine) discussed in the preceding section. Another example of this is the formation of the acetylide ion:

$$HC \equiv CH + NH_2^- \rightarrow HC \equiv C :^- + NH_3$$

Reactions of Metal-Ammonia Solutions. In an earlier section in this chapter the phenomenon of solubility of the alkali and alkaline earth metals in liquid ammonia to give blue solutions containing ammoniated electrons was discussed. These solutions are excellent strong reducing agents and, since many compounds are soluble in liquid ammonia, liquid ammonia provides for these substances the possibility of a strong, reducing agent with which the substance undergoing reduction can form a single, homogeneous phase. This is particularly significant in view of the fact that reducing agents stronger than hydrogen react with water to liberate hydrogen and, therefore, cannot generally be used in aqueous solution. A great many reactions, therefore, have been carried out in metal-ammonia solutions.

A great many direct combinations of free elements with an alkali or alkaline earth metals have been carried out by adding the free element to the appropriate metal-ammonia solution. Usually the first step in the process is to form the simple binary compound which corresponds to the normal oxidation state of the element. Commonly, further reaction occurs with an excess of the element to yield salts containing homopolyatomic anions. Table 2.9 lists some examples.

Solutions of metals in liquid ammonia are quickly decolorized by ammonium salts since ammonium ions are rapidly reduced to ammonia and free hydrogen.

$$NH_4^+ + e^-_{(am)} \rightarrow NH_3 + \tfrac{1}{2}H_2$$

Solutions of alkali metals in liquid ammonia react with other acids also, some of them very weak. For example, the following reactions have been reported:

$$SO_2\begin{array}{c} \diagup NH_2 \\ \diagdown NH_2 \end{array} + 2e^-_{(am)} \rightarrow SO_2\begin{array}{c} \diagup NH^- \\ \diagdown NH^- \end{array} + H_2$$

$$GeH_4 + e^-_{(am)} \rightarrow GeH_3^- + \tfrac{1}{2}H_2$$

$$PH_3 + e^-_{(am)} \rightarrow PH_2^- + \tfrac{1}{2}H_2$$

$$AsH_3 + e^-_{(am)} \rightarrow AsH_2^- + \tfrac{1}{2}H_2$$

TABLE 2.9 Reactions of Metal-Ammonia Solutions with Elements

Metal-Ammonia Solution	Element	Formulas of Products
Li	O_2	Li_2O, Li_2O_2
Na		Na_2O, Na_2O_2, NaO_2
K		K_2O_2, KO_2
Rb		Rb_2O, Rb_2O_2, RbO_2
Cs		Cs_2O, Cs_2O_2, Cs_2O_3, CsO_2
Ba		BaO, BaO_2
Li	S_8	Li_2S, Li_2S_2, Li_2S_4, Li_2S_x
Na		Na_2S, Na_2S_2, Na_2S_3, Na_2S_4, Na_2S_5, Na_2S_6, Na_2S_7, Na_2S_x
K		K_2S, K_2S_2, K_2S_4, K_2S_5, K_2S_x
Rb		Rb_2S
Cs		Cs_2S
Ca		CaS, CaS_x
Li	Se	Li_2Se, Li_2Se_2, Li_2Se_3, Li_2Se_4, Li_2Se_5
Na		Na_2Se, Na_2Se_2, Na_2Se_3, Na_2Se_4, Na_2Se_5, Na_2Se_6
K		K_2Se, K_2Se_2, K_2Se_3, K_2Se_4, K_2Se_x
Rb		Rb_2Se
Cs		Cs_2Se
Na	Te	Na_2Te, Na_2Te_2, Na_2Te_3
K		K_2Te, K_2Te_3
Rb		Rb_2Te
Cs		Cs_2Te
Na	P	$Na_3P_2H_3$ (Na in excess)
K		$NaP_3 \cdot 3NH_3$ (P in excess)
Li	As	Li_3As
Na		Na_3As, $Na_3As \cdot NH_3$
K		$K_3As \cdot NH_3$ (K in excess)
		$K_2As_4 \cdot NH_3$ (As in excess)
Li	Sb	Li_3Sb, $Li_3Sb \cdot NH_3$
Na		Na_3Sb, Na_3Sb_{5-7}
Na	Bi	Na_3Bi, Na_3Bi_3, Na_3Bi_{5-7}
Na	Ge	Na_4Ge_x
Li	Pb	Li_4Pb_x
Na		$NaPb_4 \cdot 2NH_3$, $NaPb$, $NaPb_2$, Na_4Pb_9
K		KPb_2, $K_4Pb_9 \cdot xNH_3$
Na	Hg	$NaHg_8$
K		KHg_{18}

The sodium derivatives of the above hydrides readily react with alkyl halides to give alkyl substituted hydrides. Consider, for example, the following sequence of reactions:

$$AsH_3 \xrightarrow[NH_{3(l)}]{e^-_{(am)}} AsH_2^- \xrightarrow[NH_{3(l)}]{RX} RAsH_2 \xrightarrow[NH_{3(l)}]{e^-_{(am)}} RAsH^-$$

$$R'RAsH \xleftarrow[NH_{3(l)}]{R'X}$$

Metal oxides or halides react with solutions of alkali metals in liquid ammonia to yield free metals, intermetallic phases containing the metal from the halide plus alkali metal, or homopolyatomic anions containing the reduced metal.

Complex cyanides are reduced by metal-ammonia solutions to free metals or to cyanide complexes of the metal in a lower oxidation state. The reaction of the tetracyanatonickelate (II) complex ($Ni(CN)_4^{--}$) with potassium in liquid ammonia is a particularly interesting example. The reduction occurs stepwise:

$$Ni(CN)_4^{--} + e^-_{(am)} \rightarrow Ni(CN)_3^{--} + CN^-$$

$$Ni(CN)_3^{--} + CN^- + e^-_{(am)} \rightarrow Ni(CN)_4^{----}$$

The compound $K_4Ni(CN)_4$ has been isolated and corresponds to an oxidation state of zero for nickel. It is interesting to note that the $Ni(CN)_4^{----}$ ion and the molecule $Ni(CO)_4$ are isoelectronic. The $Ni(CN)_3^{--}$ complex contains Ni(I).

Many organic compounds undergo reduction in metal-ammonia solutions. Acetylenic hydrocarbons are converted to acetylide ions by reaction with metal-ammonia solutions if the metal is not in excess:

$$RC\equiv CH + e^-_{(am)} \rightarrow RC\equiv C^- + H$$

If an excess of the dissolved metal is present, considerable reduction to the ethylenic derivative occurs.

$$RC\equiv CH + 2H \rightarrow RCH=CH_2$$

In the presence of alkylating agents such as alkyl halides, the acetylide ion is converted to the alkylacetylene.

$$RC\equiv C^- + R'X \rightarrow RC\equiv CR' + X^-$$

The halogen is completely removed from organic halides as halide ion by metal-ammonia solutions.

$$RX + 2e^-_{(am)} \rightarrow R^- + X^-$$

In quite a number of instances the corresponding hydrocarbon is formed

$$R^- + NH_3 \rightarrow RH + NH_2^-$$

In other cases the unsaturated hydrocarbon is obtained as a result of a dehydrohalogenation reaction.

$$RCH_2CH_2X + NH_2^- \rightarrow RCH=CH_2 + X^- + NH_3$$

Alcohols and phenols form alkoxides and phenoxides. These are examples of the use of metal-ammonia solutions to form salts of very weak acids.

$$RCH_2OH + e^-_{(am)} \rightarrow RCH_2O^- + \tfrac{1}{2}H_2$$

$$C_6H_5OH + e^-_{(am)} \rightarrow C_6H_5O^- + \tfrac{1}{2}H_2$$

The reactions of numerous organic oxygen, nitrogen, and sulfur compounds have been investigated. Reactions of organometallic compounds of various types with metal-ammonia solutions have been studied and series of compounds containing metal-to-metal bonds prepared. The following equations are illustrative:

$$(C_6H_5)_3GeCl + 2e^-_{(am)} \rightarrow (C_6H_5)_3Ge^- + Cl^-$$

$$(C_6H_5)_3Ge^- + BrSn(CH_3)_3 \rightarrow (C_6H_5)_3GeSn(CH_3)_3 + Br^-$$

$$(CH_3)_2SnBr_2 + 4e^-_{(am)} \rightarrow (CH_3)_3Sn^{--} + 2Br^-$$

$$2(CH_3)_2Sn^{--} + (CH_3)_2SnBr_2 \searrow ^{-2Br^-}$$

$$
\begin{array}{c}
\text{CH}_3\ \text{CH}_3\ \text{CH}_3 \\
|\quad\ |\quad\ | \\
\text{CH}_3\text{CH}_2-\text{Sn}-\text{Sn}-\text{Sn}-\text{CH}_2\text{CH}_3 \\
|\quad\ |\quad\ | \\
\text{CH}_3\ \text{CH}_3\ \text{CH}_3 \\
+2\text{Br}^-
\end{array}
\xleftarrow{2C_2H_5Br}
\begin{array}{c}
\text{CH}_3\ \text{CH}_3\ \text{CH}_3 \\
|\quad\ |\quad\ | \\
^-\text{Sn}-\text{Sn}-\text{Sn}^- \\
|\quad\ |\quad\ | \\
\text{CH}_3\ \text{CH}_3\ \text{CH}_3
\end{array}
$$

$$\searrow ^{+2(CH_3)_3SnBr}$$

$$
\begin{array}{c}
\text{CH}_3\ \text{CH}_3\ \text{CH}_3\ \text{CH}_3\ \text{CH}_3 \\
|\quad\ |\quad\ |\quad\ |\quad\ | \\
\text{CH}_3-\text{Sn}-\text{Sn}-\text{Sn}-\text{Sn}-\text{Sn}-\text{CH}_3 + 2\text{Br}^- \\
|\quad\ |\quad\ |\quad\ |\quad\ | \\
\text{CH}_3\ \text{CH}_3\ \text{CH}_3\ \text{CH}_3\ \text{CH}_3
\end{array}
$$

Other examples of metal-ammonia reactions with organo-metallic compounds include the following:

$$(CH_3)_3SnNH_2 + 2Na^+ + 2e^-_{(am)} \rightarrow [(CH_3)_3Sn]^-, Na^+ + NaNH_2$$

$$(CH_3)_3SnOH + 2Na^+ + 2e^-_{(am)} \rightarrow [(CH_3)_3Sn]^-, Na^+ + NaOH$$

Ammonolytic Reactions in Liquid Ammonia. Because of the concentration effect and because of the absence of competing solvolytic processes, liquid ammonia provides the ideal solvent medium for many ammonolyses. A few specific examples of ammonolytic reactions in liquid ammonia will be presented in order to illustrate the range of this type of solvent application.

Alkali metal and alkaline earth metal hydrides are ammonolyzed to the corresponding metal amide and hydrogen

$$M^+, H^- + NH_3 \rightarrow M^+, NH_2^- + H_2$$

Inorganic halogen compounds behave in liquid ammonia in a manner analogous to their behavior in aqueous solution. Ionic halides do not, in general, tend to undergo ammonolysis in liquid ammonia. However, many covalent halides ammonolyze in liquid ammonia. In some instances elevated pressure and temperature are required to carry out the reactions. The following examples are illustrative:

$$HgCl_2 \xrightarrow{NH_{3(l)}} Hg(NH_2)Cl$$

$$BCl_3 \xrightarrow{NH_{3(l)}} \begin{cases} B(NH_2)_3 \\ B_2(NH)_3 \end{cases}$$

$$CCl_4 \xrightarrow[\substack{\text{elevated} \\ \text{P \& T}}]{NH_{3(l)}} C(NH)(NH_2)_2$$

$$SiCl_4 \xrightarrow{NH_{3(l)}} Si(NH_2)_4$$

$$SiH_3Cl \xrightarrow{NH_{3(l)}} N(SiH_3)_3$$

$$GeI_4 \xrightarrow{NH_{3(l)}} Ge(NH)_2$$

$$VOCl_3 \xrightarrow{NH_{3(l)}} VO(NH_2)_3$$

$$PCl_3 \xrightarrow{NH_{3(l)}} P(NH_2)_3 \xrightarrow{0°C} P_2(NH)_3$$

Organic halides undergo slow ammonolysis at the boiling point of liquid ammonia to yield mixtures of primary, secondary, and tertiary amines.

$$RX + 2NH_3 \rightarrow RNH_2 + NH_4X$$

$$RX + RNH_2 + NH_3 \rightarrow R_2NH + NH_4X$$

$$RX + R_2NH + NH_3 \rightarrow R_3N + NH_4X$$

$$(X = halogen)$$

Liquid ammonia favors the formation of the primary amine much more than do other ammonolytic media such as alcoholic ammonia. The organic iodides are more readily solvolyzed than the other organic halides.

Examples of other types of ammonolyses of organic compounds are given in Table 2.10.

TABLE 2.10.   Ammonolyses of Organic Compounds in Liquid Ammonia

Compound	Ammonolysis Product(s)
ROH	No ammonolysis in liquid ammonia.

$$\begin{matrix} CH_2CN \\ | \\ OH \end{matrix} \qquad \begin{matrix} CH_2CN \\ | \\ NH_2 \end{matrix}$$

$$CH_3C\underset{NH_2}{\overset{O}{\diagdown}} \qquad CH_3C\underset{NH_2}{\overset{NH}{\diagup}} \left. \right\} \text{Require presence of } NH_4^+ \text{ in}$$

$$H_2NCN \qquad C\underset{\diagdown NH_2}{\overset{\diagup NH_2}{=NH}} \left. \right\} \text{the liquid ammonia}$$

$$\begin{matrix} \overset{O}{\diagup} \\ C{-}OC_2H_5 \\ | \\ C{-}OC_2H_5 \\ \diagdown O \end{matrix} \qquad \begin{matrix} \overset{O}{\diagup} \\ C{-}NH_2 \\ | \\ C{-}NH_2 \\ \diagdown O \end{matrix}$$

$$C_6H_5C\overset{O}{\diagdown}_{OC_2H_5} \qquad C_6H_5C\overset{O}{\diagdown}{-}NH_2 \quad \text{Catalyzed by } NH_4^+ \text{ salts}$$

$$CH_2{=}CHC\overset{O}{\diagdown}_{OCH_3} \quad \left\{ \begin{matrix} H_2NCH_2CH_2C\overset{O}{\diagdown}{-}OCH_3 \\ \\ HN(CH_2CH_2C\overset{O}{\diagdown}{-}OCH_3)_2 \\ \\ N(CH_2CH_2C\overset{O}{\diagdown}{-}OCH_3)_3 \\ \\ HN(CH_2CH_2C\overset{O}{\diagup}{-}NH_2)_2 \\ \\ N(CH_2CH_2C\overset{O}{\diagup}{-}NH_2)_3 \end{matrix} \right.$$

(continued)

TABLE 2.10. (*Continued*)

Compound	Ammonolysis Product(s)
$XCH_2\overset{O}{\underset{\|}{C}}-OR$	$XCH_2\overset{O}{\underset{\|}{C}}-NH_2$ $\begin{cases} \text{As } X \text{ changes, the rate of am-} \\ \text{monolysis decreases with} \\ \text{change in the nature of } X \text{ in} \\ \text{the order } NC->H_2N\overset{O}{\underset{\|}{C}}-> \\ C_2H_5O\overset{O}{\underset{\|}{C}}->C_2H_5O-> \\ C_6H_5->H- \end{cases}$
R_2NCN	$H_2NCN + RNH_2$ Catalyzed by KNH_2

Summary of the Solvent Characteristics of Liquid Ammonia

Liquid ammonia is a solvent in which organic compounds are generally more soluble than in water but in which ionic substances tend to be somewhat less soluble than in water. Liquid ammonia makes available stronger bases than are available in aqueous solutions, but only relatively weak acids are available in liquid ammonia chemistry. The strongly reducing metal-ammonia solutions make liquid ammonia an excellent solvent for many reduction reactions. Strong oxidizing agents react with ammonia, however, and thus may not be used in liquid ammonia solutions. Liquid ammonia is an excellent choice of solvent for many ammonolytic reactions.

Selected Readings

1. Audrieth, L. F., and Kleinberg, J., "Non-Aqueous Solvents," Chaps. 3, 4, 5, and 6. John Wiley & Sons, Inc., New York. 1953.
2. Cotton, F. A., "Metal-Ammonia Solutions" by W. L. Jolly, pp. 235–282, *in* "Progress in Inorganic Chemistry," Vol. 1, Interscience Publishers, Inc., New York. 1959.

3. Emeléus, A. J., and Anderson, J., "Modern Aspects of Inorganic Chemistry," 3rd Ed., pp. 367–374, D. Van Nostrand Co., Inc., New York (1960).

4. Jander, G., "Die Chemie in Wasserähnlichen Lösungsmitteln," Chap. 3, Springer-Verlag, Berlin, 1949.

5. Watt, G., *Chem. Reviews*, **46**, (2), 289–379 (1950).

_____

chapter three

REACTIONS
IN SULFURIC ACID

WHEREAS IN THE PRECEDING chapter we studied a solvent with a basicity much greater than water, now we shall consider the chemistry of reactions in sulfuric acid, a solvent much more acidic than water.

The pioneer work in sulfuric acid as a solvent was carried out by A. Hantzsch during the first decade of this century. Major advances in this study resulted from the work of L. Hammett in the early 1930's. During the past dozen years, however, our knowledge of chemistry in this solvent has been greatly expanded through the excellent work of R. J. Gillespie and his colleagues.

Sulfuric acid is a very good solvent for numerous organic compounds, many of which are able to accept protons, i.e., act as bases, in it. Because of its strongly acidic character, sulfuric acid may be used as a solvent in which very weak bases, such as ketones and aromatic nitro-compounds, are acidic enough to act as proton donors toward sulfuric acid molecules.

Physical Properties of Sulfuric Acid

Some of the more important physical constants for sulfuric acid are listed in Table 3.1.

TABLE 3.1. Physical Constants of Sulfuric Acid

Freezing Point	10.371° C
Boiling Point	290–317° C
Density, $d_4{}^{25°}$	1.8269
Viscosity (25° C)	24.54 centipoise
Heat Capacity	0.338 cal./deg./g.
Heat of Fusion	2560 cal./mole
Dielectric Constant (10° C)	120.
Dielectric Constant (25° C)	100.
Specific Conductance (25° C)	0.010439 ohm^{-1}cm^{-1}

Pure sulfuric acid is prepared by adding aqueous sulfuric acid to fuming sulfuric acid (anhydrous sulfuric acid containing excess sulfur trioxide) until a maximum freezing point of 10.371° C is obtained. Sulfuric acid is, as its high viscosity and high boiling point indicate, a highly associated solvent. Study of the crystalline solid indicates a layer structure in which each sulfuric acid molecule is hydrogen bonded to four other such molecules, the length of these bonds being 2.85 A. It may reasonably be assumed that this association persists to a large extent in the liquid state.

The sulfuric acid molecule has the tetrahedral structure indicated in Fig. 3.1. This structure may be rationalized on the basis of the use by the sulfur atom of sp^3 hybrid orbitals in the formation of bonds with the four oxygen atoms. Since d orbitals are also available on the sulfur atom and unshared

Fig. 3.1. The structure of the H_2SO_4 molecule. (From Sisler, VanderWerf, and Davidson, "College Chemistry, a Systematic Approach," MacMillan, N. Y., 2nd Edition, 1961.)

electrons on the oxygen atoms, it is probable that the sulfur to oxygen bond have considerable π bond character.

Equilibria in 100% Sulfuric Acid

The relatively high specific conductance of 100% sulfuric acid (1.0439×10^{-2} ohm^{-1}cm^{-1} at 25°C) is an indication of a considerable degree of autoionization. Just as in water we have dissociation according to the equation

$$2H_2O \rightleftharpoons H_3O^+ + OH^-$$

and in liquid ammonia autoionization according to the equation

$$2NH_3 \rightleftharpoons NH_4^+ + NH_2^-$$

in sulfuric acid we have the equilibrium

$$2H_2SO_4 \rightleftharpoons H_3SO_4^+ + HSO_4^-$$

The ion product constant for sulfuric acid $K = [H_3SO_4^+][HSO_4^-]$ has the value 2.4×10^{-4} at 25°C, which is higher than that of the ion-product constant for the autoionization of any other solvent for which data are known.

There are, in addition to the autoionization equilibrium, other dissociation equilibria which are important. Among the most important of these is the self-dissociation reaction.

$$2H_2SO_4 \rightleftharpoons H_2O + H_2S_2O_7$$

Since water is basic toward sulfuric acid, and disulfuric acid ($H_2S_2O_7$) is acidic toward sulfuric acid, the two further equilibria must be considered:

$$H_2O + H_2SO_4 \rightleftharpoons H_3O^+ + HSO_4^-$$

$$H_2SO_4 + H_2S_2O_7 \rightleftharpoons H_3SO_4^+ + HS_2O_7^-$$

The first of these proceeds extensively to the right and the second to a small extent only. From the four equilibria mentioned above the additional equilibrium

$$2H_2SO_4 \rightleftharpoons H_3O^+ + HS_2O_7^-$$

may be derived.

Studies of the freezing points and electrical conductivities of solutions of metal hydrogen sulfates, disulfuric acid, and water in sulfuric acid have made it possible to estimate the value of equilibrium constants for the various dissociation equilibria. These constants are listed in Table 3.2.

TABLE 3.2.   Equilibrium Constants for Dissociation Reactions in Sulfuric Acid

Equation	Equilibrium Constant Expression	Value of Constant
$2H_2SO_4 \rightleftharpoons H_3SO_4^+ + HSO_4^-$	$K = [H_3SO_4^+][HSO_4^-]$	1.7×10^{-4} (10°C) 2.4×10^{-4} (25°C)
$2H_2SO_4 \rightleftharpoons H_3O^+ + HS_2O_7^-$	$K' = [H_3O^+][HS_2O_7^-]$	3.5×10^{-5} (10°C) 4.0×10^{-5} (25°C)
$H_2S_2O_7 + H_2SO_4 \rightleftharpoons H_3SO_4^+ + HS_2O_7^-$	$K'' = \dfrac{[H_3SO_4^+][HS_2O_7]}{[H_2S_2O_7]}$	1.4×10^{-2} (10°C) 1.4×10^{-2} (25°C)
$H_2O + H_2SO_4 \rightleftharpoons H_3O^+ + HSO_4^-$	$K''' = \dfrac{[H_3O^+][HSO_4^-]}{[H_2O]}$	1 (10°C) 1 (25°C)

The total molar concentration of species other than H_2SO_4 (i.e., HSO_4^-, $H_3SO_4^+$, H_3O^+, $HS_2O_7^-$, $H_2S_2O_7$, H_2O) in 100% sulfuric acid at 25°C is calculated to be 0.0490 M.

Because of the leveling effect of the highly acidic solvent sulfuric acid, the strongest base which can exist in solution in 100% sulfuric acid is the hydrogen sulfate ion, HSO_4^-, a very weak base indeed. Stronger bases than this undergo immediate solvolysis yielding the hydrogen sulfate ion.

$$B: + H_2SO_4 \rightarrow B:H^+ + HSO_4^-$$

Examples of this phenomenon include the dissolving of sodium hydroxide, potassium acetate, sodium amide, or even sodium chloride in sulfuric acid.

$$OH^- + H_2SO_4 \rightarrow H_2O + HSO_4^-$$

$$\xrightarrow{H_2SO_4} H_3O^+ + HSO_4^-$$

$$CH_3COO^- + H_2SO_4 \rightarrow CH_3COOH + HSO_4^-$$

$$\xrightarrow{H_2SO_4} CH_3C(OH)_2^+ + HSO_4^-$$

$$NH_2^- + H_2SO_4 \rightarrow NH_3 + HSO_4^-$$

$$\xrightarrow{H_2SO_4} NH_4^+ + HSO_4^-$$

$$Cl^- + H_2SO_4 \rightarrow HCl + HSO_4^-$$

On the other hand, exceedingly strong acids are capable of existence in 100% sulfuric acid, for the limit of acid strength in this solvent is that of the ion $H_3SO_4^+$, a highly acidic species. Stronger proton donors than $H_3SO_4^+$ react with sulfuric acid in accordance with the equation

$$H:A + H_2SO_4 \rightleftharpoons H_3SO_4^+ + :A^-$$

but there are very few acids of sufficient strength to enter into this type of reaction with sulfuric acid. Some of these are discussed below.

Solubilities in Sulfuric Acid

Most solutions in 100% sulfuric acid are electrolytic. Because of the high degree of hydrogen bonding between the sulfuric acid molecules, it is difficult for a solute to disrupt the sulfuric acid molecular aggregation unless the solute is highly solvated. Such solvation results only when the solution is ionic (or reacts with the solvent to form ions) or is itself strongly hydrogen bonded to sulfuric acid molecules. Thus, in order for a substance to behave as a non-electrolyte in 100% sulfuric acid it must be so weakly basic as to not accept protons from sulfuric acid but must be capable of forming hydrogen bonds with sulfuric acid. Only a few such substances are known; they include a few polynitro-aromatic compounds, sulfuryl chloride, and picric acid.

Sulfuric acid is, however, as its high dielectric constant would indicate, an excellent solvent for electrolytes. Because of the highly acidic character of the solvent and its ability to bring about solvolysis, many of the solution processes involve the formation of several different ions or molecules from a single solute molecule. The following equations are illustrative. Listed with each is the number (μ) of ionic or molecular species formed from one solute molecule. The values of μ were determined cryoscopically.

$$\mu$$

$$C_6H_4(NH_2)_2 + 2H_2SO_4 \rightarrow C_6H_4(NH_3)_2^{++} + 2HSO_4^- \qquad 3$$

$$CH_3COOH + H_2SO_4 \rightarrow CH_3C(OH)_2^+ + HSO_4^- \qquad 2$$

$$C_2H_5OH + 2H_2SO_4 \rightarrow C_2H_5OSO_3H + H_3O^+ + HSO_4^- \qquad 3$$

$$NO_2OH + 2H_2SO_4 \rightarrow NO_2^+ + H_3O^+ + 2HSO_4^- \qquad 4$$

$$B(OH)_3 + 6H_2SO_4 \rightarrow 3H_3O^+ + B(OSO_3H)_4^- + 2HSO_4^- \qquad 6$$

$$N_2O_4 + 3H_2SO_4 \rightarrow NO^+ + NO_2^+ + H_3O^+ + 3HSO_4^- \qquad 6$$

Many inorganic salts are soluble in sulfuric acid but almost without exception solvolysis occurs during the solution process. Thus, the substances Li_2SO_4, $NaNO_3$, Na_2HAsO_4, KNO_3, $KSCN$, K_2SO_4, $K_4[Fe(CN)_6]$, $K_3[Fe(CN)_6]$, $AgNO_3$, Ag_2SO_4, CaF_2, $Ca_3(PO_4)_2$, and $BaSO_4$, all dissolve in 100% sulfuric acid with no visible reaction at room temperature, but in each of these cases solvolysis occurs. Among difficultly soluble salts are $CaCO_3$ (CO_2 evolves), Hg_2SO_4, $MgSO_4$, $ZnSO_4$, $PbSO_4$, $CuSO_4$, $HgSO_4$, and $FeSO_4$. Apparently insoluble salts include $AgCl$, $CuBr_2$ (liberates Br_2 on heating), $NiSO_4$, $AlCl_3$, $AlPO_4$, $Al_2(SO_4)_3$, and $Fe_2(SO_4)_3$.

In some instances solvolysis is immediately apparent. With the alkali or alkaline earth halides immediate evolution of hydrogen halide (with chlorides) or free halogen (with bromides) is observable. With Na_2SiO_3, $Al(NO_3)_3$, $Fe(NO_3)_3$, and $Fe_4[Fe(CN)_6]_3$ solvolysis yields a solid product.

Sulfuric acid readily forms solvates with various solutes which are dissolved in 100% sulfuric acid. Table 3.3 lists the solubilities of several metal sulfates in sulfuric acid at 25° C. The formulas for the solvated sulfates constituting the solid phases in equilibrium with such solutions are listed also.

TABLE 3.3. Solubilities of Metal Sulfates in Sulfuric Acid at 25° C

	Soly. (Mole Fraction)	Solid Phase
Li_2SO_4	.1428	$2LiHSO_4 \cdot H_2SO_4$
Na_2SO_4	.0528	$4NaHSO_4 \cdot 7H_2SO_4$
K_2SO_4	.0928	$KHSO_4 \cdot H_2SO_4$
$MgSO_4$	.0018	$Mg(HSO_4)_2 \cdot 2H_2SO_4$
$CaSO_4$	.0516	$Ca(HSO_4)_2 \cdot 2H_2SO_4$
$BaSO_4$	.0885	$Ba(HSO_4)_2 \cdot 2H_2SO_4$
$CuSO_4$	.0008	$CuSO_4$
Ag_2SO_4	.0911	$2AgHSO_4 \cdot H_2SO_4$
Hg_2SO_4	.0078	$Hg_2(HSO_4)_2$
$HgSO_4$	.0002	$HgSO_4$
$PbSO_4$	.012	$PbSO_4$
$ZnSO_4$	.0017	. . .
$FeSO_4$	.0017	. . .

In addition to the sulfates listed in the table, the following sulfates have solubilities greater than a mole fraction of .02 at 25° C: $SrSO_4$, Rb_2SO_4, Ca_2SO_4, Tl_2SO_4, and $(NH_4)_2SO_4$. There is some parallelism between the solubilities of various sulfates in sulfuric acid and the solubilities of hydroxides in water and of acetates in anhydrous acetic acid.

Conductances in Sulfuric Acid

Mobilities of various cations and anions in 100% sulfuric acid would, because of the high viscosity of their solvent, be expected to be quite low and indeed this is, in general, true. Consider, for example, the relative mobilities in sulfuric acid and in water of the first four ions listed in Table 3.4.

TABLE 3.4.   Ion Mobilities at Infinite Dilution in Sulfuric Acid and in Water at 25°C

Ion	H_2SO_4	H_2O
Na^+	~ 3	50.1
K^+	~ 5	73.5
Ba^{++}	~ 2	63.6
H_3O^+	~ 5	349.8
OH^-	. . .	198.6
$H_3SO_4^+$	242	. . .
HSO_4^-	171	. . .

The same table shows, however, that the $H_3SO_4^+$ ion and the HSO_4^- ion have very high mobilities in sulfuric acid. In fact, it is because of the high mobilities of these two kinds of ions, as well as because of the considerable degree of ionic dissociation of sulfuric acid, that this solvent has quite an appreciable electrical conductance in spite of its high viscosity. The abnormally high mobility of the HSO_4^- ion is evidenced also by the very low transport numbers* (t^+) of the cations in solutions of various metal hydrogen sulfates in 100% sulfuric acid. Some of these values are listed in Table 3.5. The abnormally high mobilities of the $H_3SO_4^+$ and HSO_4^- ions in sulfuric acid solutions are analogous to the abnormally high mobilities of the H_3O^+ and OH^- ions in aqueous solution and a cor-

TABLE 3.5.   Transport Numbers for Various Metal Hydrogen Sulfates in Solution in Sulfuric Acid

Electrolyte	Molality	t^+	t^-
$LiHSO_4$	0.556	0.013	0.987
$NaHSO_4$	0.792	0.021	0.979
$KHSO_4$	0.624	0.030	0.970
$AgHSO_4$	0.249	0.026	0.974
$Sr(HSO_4)_2$	0.211	0.007	0.993
$Ba(HSO_4)_2$	0.174	0.009	0.991

*Transport numbers measure the relative amounts of current carried by the cation and anion of a given electrolyte. A low t^+ value indicates that the cation moves much more slowly than the anion and hence conducts only a very small fraction of the total current.

respondingly analogous explanation is offered for this behavior. In aqueous media we picture water molecules connected in a network by hydrogen bonds

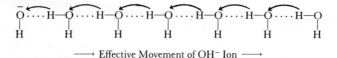

⟶ Effective Motion of H_3O^+ Ion ⟶

The effective movement of an H_3O^+ ion through the aqueous solution can be brought above by the very minor shifts of protons along the chain in the manner indicated by the arrows. The actual mass motion involved in this process is very slight and the process, therefore, occurs quite rapidly. A similar mechanism applies to the mobility of OH^- ions:

$$\bar{O} \cdots H{-}O \cdots H{-}O \cdots H{-}O \cdots H{-}O \cdots H{-}O \cdots H{-}O$$

⟶ Effective Movement of OH^- Ion ⟶

In 100% sulfuric acid the H_2SO_4 molecules are similarly connected in hydrogen-bonded networks. We can visualize the effective movement of $H_3SO_4^+$ and HSO_4^- through such networks by means of proton-transfer mechanisms analogous to those already described for H_3O^+ and OH^- in aqueous systems.

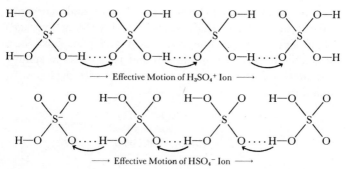

⟶ Effective Motion of $H_3SO_4^+$ Ion ⟶

⟶ Effective Motion of HSO_4^- Ion ⟶

Because of these very high mobilities of $H_3SO_4^+$ and HSO_4^- the electrical conductances of various acids and bases in 100% sulfuric acid are principally determined by the number of $H_3SO_4^+$ or HSO_4^- ions per mole of the particular acid or base in the sulfuric acid solution. Thus, measurement of electrical conductances provides valuable information concerning the ionization processes for certain electrolytes.

Acid-Base Reactions in Sulfuric Acid

Bases. The strongest base which can exist in solution in 100% sulfuric acid is the hydrogen sulfate ion HSO_4^-. Hence, "strong" bases in the system are solutes which yield high concentrations of this ion in sulfuric acid solution. These include, in the first place, metal hydrogen sulfates, $MHSO_4$, which are analogous to metal hydroxides in the aqueous system. Since the anions of normal salts of most of the inorganic acids are actually stronger bases than is the hydrogen sulfate ion, such salts undergo complete solvolysis in sulfuric acid to yield hydrogen sulfate solutions. The following equations represent examples:

$$Na^+,Cl^- + H_2SO_4 \rightarrow Na^+ + HSO_4^- + HCl$$

$$3Na^+,PO_4^\equiv + 3H_2SO_4 \rightarrow 3Na^+ + 3HSO_4^- + H_3PO_4$$

$$Na^+,NO_3^- + H_2SO_4 \rightarrow Na^+ + HSO_4^- + HNO_3$$

Many covalent compounds, both organic and inorganic, undergo protolysis in 100% sulfuric acid yielding hydrogen sulfate ions. For example, nitric acid and phosphoric acid formed by the solvolysis of nitrates and phosphates in sulfuric acid undergo further reaction in accordance with the following equations:

$$NO_2OH + 2H_2SO_4 \rightarrow NO_2^+ + H_3O^+ + 2HSO_4^-$$

$$PO(OH)_3 + H_2SO_4 \rightarrow P(OH)_4^+ + HSO_4^-$$

Thus, both these compounds exhibit basic behavior in sulfuric acid. Other examples include amides,

$$C_6H_5CONH_2 + H_2SO_4 \rightarrow C_6H_5CONH_3^+ + HSO_4^-$$

esters,

$$C_6H_5C{\overset{\displaystyle O}{\diagup}}OC_2H_5 + H_2SO_4 \rightarrow C_6H_5C{\overset{\displaystyle OH}{\diagup}}OC_2H_5^+ + HSO_4^-$$

carboxylic acids,

$$CH_3COOH + H_2SO_4 \rightarrow CH_3C(OH)_2^+ + HSO_4^-$$

ketones,

$$CH_3C{\overset{\displaystyle O}{\diagup}}C_6H_5 + H_2SO_4 \rightarrow CH_3C{\overset{\displaystyle OH^+}{\diagup}}C_6H_5 + HSO_4^-$$

amines,

$$C_6H_5NH_2 + H_2SO_4 \rightarrow C_6H_5NH_3^+ + HSO_4^-$$

phosphines,

$$(C_6H_5)_3P + H_2SO_4 \rightarrow (C_6H_5)_3PH^+ + HSO_4^-$$

In many instances the initial protolysis is followed by further reactions yielding more complex systems, as is the case with nitric acid above. Further examples of complex ionization processes include the following:

$$C_2H_5OH + 2H_2SO_4 \rightarrow C_2H_5OSO_3H + H_3O^+ + HSO_4^-$$

$$(C_6H_5)_3COH + 2H_2SO_4 \rightarrow (C_6H_5)_3C^+ + H_3O^+ + 2HSO_4^-$$

$$(CH_3)_3SiOSi(CH_3)_3 + 3H_2SO_4 \rightarrow$$
$$2(CH_3)SiOSO_3H + H_3O^+ + HSO_4^-$$

$$B(OH)_3 + 6H_2SO_4 \rightarrow 3H_3O^+ + B(OSO_3H)_4^- + 2HSO_4^-$$

Some of the organic compounds which act as bases in anhydrous sulfuric acid react only partially with sulfuric acid and hence act as weak bases. The ionization equilibria of a number of these weak bases are represented by the following equations:

$$K_{\text{Ion}}$$

$$CH_3CN + H_2SO_4 \rightleftharpoons CH_3CNH^+ + HSO_4^- \qquad 1.6 \times 10^{-1}$$

$$C_6H_5NO_2 + H_2SO_4 \rightleftharpoons C_6H_5NO_2H^+ + HSO_4^- \qquad 1.0 \times 10^{-2}$$

$$CH_3NO_2 + H_2SO_4 \rightleftharpoons CH_3NO_2H^+ + HSO_4^- \qquad 2.5 \times 10^{-3}$$

$$(C_6H_5)_2SO + H_2SO_4 \rightleftharpoons (C_6H_5)_2SOH^+ + HSO_4^- \qquad 1.6 \times 10^{-2}$$

Conductimetric, cryoscopic, spectroscopic, and titrimetric measurements of the ionization constants of several of these weak bases in sulfuric acid have been made, and for a given compound the results obtained by the various methods in general agree closely. The ionization constants listed above were measured by one or more of these methods.

Acids. Since there are few compounds which have sufficiently strong proton-donor tendencies to transfer protons to H_2SO_4 molecules, there are few compounds capable of acting as acids in solution in 100% sulfuric acid.

Among these relatively few acids in the sulfuric acid solvent system are disulfuric acid ($H_2S_2O_7$), trisulfuric acid ($H_2S_3O_{10}$), and higher polysulfuric acids of the general formula $H_2SO_4(SO_3)_n$. A 0.1 molar solution of disulfuric acid is 3.0% ionized in accordance with the equation:

$$H_2S_2O_7 + H_2SO_4 \rightleftharpoons H_3SO_4^+ + HS_2O_7^-$$

Several other acids are found among the hydrogen sulfate complexes. Several of the acids are listed in Table 3.6 with values for their ionization constants.

Acid-Base Titrations. A number of acid-base titrations have been carried out in 100% sulfuric acid solution. Such titrations are most conveniently followed conductometrically. This is possible because the $H_3SO_4^+$ and HSO_4^- ions have

TABLE 3.6. Acids in the Sulfuric Acid Solvent System

	K_{Ion}
HAs(OSO$_3$H)$_4$	very weak
HPb(OSO$_3$H)$_6$$^-$	1.8×10^{-3} (10° C)
HSO$_3$F	3×10^{-3} (25° C)
H$_2$S$_2$O$_7$	1.4×10^{-2} (10° C)
H$_2$Pb(OSO$_3$H)$_6$	1.1×10^{-2} (10° C)
H$_2$S$_3$O$_{10}$	moderately strong
HB(OSO$_3$H)$_4$	strong

much higher conductances in sulfuric acid than any other cations or anions. Hence, a minimum conductance occurs at or very near the equivalence point in the neutralization reaction:

$$H_3SO_4^+ + HSO_4^- \rightarrow 2H_2SO_4$$

If either the acid or base involved in the titration is only partially dissociated (i.e., is a weak acid or base) the minimum point will not occur at the equivalence point, and corrections will have to be made. In general, it has been demonstrated that for an acid-base titration in 100% sulfuric acid, the molar ratio of base to acid (n_b/n_a) at the minimum conductance at 25 °C is given by the equation

$$n_b/n_a = 0.98(1 + 0.017/K_b)\ (1 + 0.014/K_a)$$

where K_b and K_a refer to the ionization constants of the respective base and acid.

Summary of the Solvent Characteristics of Sulfuric Acid

As a solvent, pure sulfuric acid is characterized by strongly acidic character, high dielectric constant, relatively high electrical conductance, high viscosity, and many instances of complex ionization of solutes. Very few substances capable of dissolving in sulfuric acid behave as non-electrolytes; many molecules behave as bases toward sulfuric acid and undergo protolysis. Many ionic compounds are soluble in sulfuric acid; however, solvolytic reactions occur with many of these substances, since most anions accept protons from sulfuric acid molecules. The strongest base available in sulfuric acid solution is the HSO_4^- ion and the strongest acid is $H_3SO_4^+$. The neutralization reaction which is characteristic of this solvent system is, therefore,

$$H_3SO_4^+ + HSO_4^- \rightleftharpoons 2 H_2SO_4$$

Selected Readings

1. Audrieth, L., and Kleinberg, J., "Non-Aqueous Solvents," pp. 172–189. John Wiley & Sons, Inc., New York, 1953.
2. Emeléus, H., and Sharpe, A., "Advances in Inorganic Chemistry and Radiochemistry," Vol. I, Academic Press, Inc., New York, 1959, pp. 385–423. (This material written by R. J. Gillespie and E. A. Robinson.)

chapter four ————————————————————

LIQUID OXIDE SOLVENT SYSTEMS

ALL OF THE SOLVENTS thus far considered belong to a class of liquids commonly described as amphiprotic. A molecule of such a solvent is capable, under one set of circumstances, of accepting a proton, and under other conditions of donating a proton to another molecule or ion. We shall now consider two solvents, dinitrogen tetroxide and sulfur dioxide, which contain no hydrogen atoms. Each of these solvents may be considered to be the parent substance for a system of compounds. As we shall see, it is desirable to use the Lewis definition of acids and bases (acids are electron acceptors; bases are electron donors) in discussing chemical reactions in these solvents since the Brønsted definitions cannot be applied to substances which do not contain hydrogen.

A. REACTIONS IN LIQUID DINITROGEN TETROXIDE

Because of its convenient liquid range, its very interesting chemical characteristics, as well as its ease of preparation and purification, dinitrogen tetroxide has, during the past quarter century, been the subject of much research as a medium for chemical reactions and as a reactant in the liquid phase.

The character of dinitrogen tetroxide as a medium for carrying out chemical reactions is determined principally by: (1) its low dielectric constant (2.42 at 18° C) which makes it a

poor solvent for ionic compounds; (2) the variety of dissociation equilibria which it exhibits; (3) its Lewis acid character;
and (4) its oxidizing properties.

Physical Constants

Dinitrogen tetroxide melts at $-12.3°$ C (the triple point is
at $-11.2°$ C) and its normal boiling point is $21.3°C$. Thus, its
liquid range is convenient for its use as a solvent. The liquid
may be readily supercooled and has been cooled as low as
$-110°$ C without it crystallizing. Its critical temperature is
$158.2°$ C and its critical pressure is 100.0 atm. The density of
dinitrogen tetroxide is 1.49 g./cc. at $0°$ C. The electrical
conductance of liquid dinitrogen tetroxide is very low; the
specific conductance at various temperatures expressed in
$ohm^{-1}cm^{-1}$ is given by the equation $\log_{10}\kappa = (-1267/T) -
8.260$. This corresponds to a value for κ of 2.36×10^{-13}
$ohm^{-1}cm^{-1}$ at $17°$ C.

Structure of Dinitrogen Tetroxide

X-ray diffraction studies of crystalline dinitrogen tetroxide
indicate the following coplanar structure:

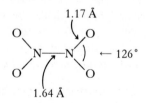

Electron diffraction studies on gaseous dinitrogen tetroxide
indicate a similar coplanar structure:

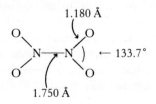

It may be noted that in each case the nitrogen to nitrogen bond distance is considerably larger than is normal for a nitrogen to nitrogen single bond. This may be rationalized if we assume that the N_2O_4 molecule is a resonance hybrid of such valence bond structures as:

in which the adjacent nitrogen atoms bear positive charges. These would cause the nitrogen to nitrogen bond to be elongated.

It is of interest to note that recent studies of the infrared spectra of solid dinitrogen tetroxide indicate the existence in detectable amounts at low temperatures of two additional forms, (a) and (b), of dinitrogen tetroxide:

(a) 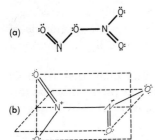   (hybridized with similar resonance forms)

(b)   (hybridized with similar resonance forms) (the two NO_2 groups are in planes which are at right angles to each other).

Equilibria in Liquid and Gaseous Dinitrogen Tetroxide

In both the liquid and gaseous states dinitrogen tetroxide is in mobile equilibrium with the brown, monomeric species, NO_2, nitrogen dioxide.

$$N_2O_4 \rightleftharpoons 2NO_2$$

Since nitrogen dioxide contains an odd number of electrons and is, therefore, paramagnetic, the change in equilibrium with change in temperature may be readily followed by measuring the magnetic susceptibility of the equilibrium mixture. Because of the differences in the absorption spectra of the monomeric and dimeric species, the equilibrium can also be studied spectrophotometrically. Results obtained by these two methods indicate that the equilibrium constant $K = \dfrac{[NO_2]^2}{[N_2O_4]}$ for the reaction $N_2O_4 \rightleftharpoons 2NO_2$ in the liquid phase is of the order of 1.0×10^{-6} g./cc. at $20°$ C. This means that the concentration of NO_2 in the liquid phase is quite low. However, in the vapor phase the concentration of NO_2 is 16.1% at the boiling point and increases rapidly as the temperature is raised.

Studies of the chemistry of liquid dinitrogen tetroxide demonstrate there is an additional equilibrium in the liquid phase, viz. the autoionization equilibrium

$$N_2O_4 \rightleftharpoons NO^+ + NO_3^-$$

The fact that this ionization occurs to only an exceedingly small extent is demonstrated by the very low magnitude of the specific electrical conductance of pure liquid dinitrogen tetroxide.

Certain chemical reactions of liquid dinitrogen tetroxide with organic compounds indicate also the probability that this substance is at least potentially capable of dissociating in accordance with the equilibrium

$$N_2O_4 \rightleftharpoons NO_2^+ + NO_2^-$$

The extent of this dissociation in pure liquid dinitrogen tetroxide is undoubtedly very small.

Solubilities in Liquid Dinitrogen Tetroxide

As would be expected from its very low dielectric constant, dinitrogen tetroxide is a poor solvent for ionic substances. In fact, solubilities in dinitrogen tetroxide are similar to corresponding solubilities in ether. Among the many organic solutes which dissolve in dinitrogen tetroxide without apparent change, we find alkanes, aromatic hydrocarbons, halo- and nitro- hydrocarbons, and carboxylic acids. Ethers, many tertiary amines, oxygen-containing and nitrogen-containing heterocyclic compounds, as well as many other oxygen-containing species, form addition compounds with dinitrogen tetroxide. Alkenes, alcohols, many amines, and ketones react with dinitrogen tetroxide. The strong oxidizing tendency of this solvent precludes its use as a solvent for many solutes with reducing properties.

Dinitrogen Tetroxide as the Basis for a Solvent System

Addison and his co-workers* have studied a number of reactions in liquid dinitrogen tetroxide from the point of view that dinitrogen tetroxide is the parent solvent for a "system of compounds" analogous to the "ammonia system" or the "water system."

Acid-Base Reactions. The dissociation equilibrium mentioned above, $N_2O_4 \rightleftharpoons NO^+ + NO_3^-$, was considered to be analogous to the autoionization reactions known or postulated for various other solvents, for example,

$$2H_2O \rightleftharpoons H_3O^+ + OH^-$$
$$2NH_3 \rightleftharpoons NH_4^+ + NH_2^-$$

According to this idea, substances furnishing the NO^+ group would be typical acids in dinitrogen tetroxide and substances furnishing NO_3^- ions would be typical bases. Such substances as $NOCl$ and $NOBr$ should behave as acids and the nitrates, e.g., $[Et_2NH_2] NO_3$ should act as bases in this system. The low dielectric constant of dinitrogen tetroxide does not favor ionic reactions. However, a solution of $NOCl$ in liquid dinitrogen tetroxide reacts with solid silver nitrate

$$NOCl + AgNO_{3(s)} \xrightarrow[N_2O_4]{liq.} AgCl_{(s)} + N_2O_4$$

*Addison, C. C., and Thompson, P. J., *J. Chem. Soc.*, **S211**, 218 (1950).

This reaction would be a typical neutralization reaction analogous to the following reactions from the water and ammonia systems:

$$(H_3O)Cl + NaOH \xrightarrow{H_2O} NaCl + 2H_2O$$

$$(NH_4)Cl + KNH_2 \xrightarrow[NH_3]{liq} KCl + 2NH_3$$

Solvolytic Reactions. A number of solvolytic reactions in liquid dinitrogen tetroxide have been investigated. Thus the salt diethyl ammonium chloride undergoes solvolysis in accordance with the following equation:

$$[Et_2NH_2]Cl + N_2O_{4(l)} \rightarrow NOCl + [Et_2NH_2]NO_3$$

The general type reaction $MCl + N_2O_4 \rightarrow NOCl + MNO_3$ is fully reversible in liquid dinitrogen tetroxide depending upon the solubility of MCl in the system, and the removal of NOCl from the system. The process for preparing NOCl from potassium chloride is in some ways analogous. In this process gaseous dinitrogen tetroxide is passed through a column of potassium chloride moistened with a trace of water. The following reaction occurs:

$$KCl_{(slightly\ moist)} + N_2O_{4(g)} \rightarrow NOCl_{(g)} + KNO_{3(s)}$$

Other solvolytic reactions in liquid dinitrogen tetroxide include the following:

$$[Mg(H_2O)_6]Cl_2 + 2N_2O_4 \rightarrow [Mg(H_2O)_6](NO_3)_2 + 2NOCl$$

$$Mg(ClO_4)_2 + 2N_2O_4 \rightarrow Mg(NO_3)_2 + 2NO(ClO_4)$$

In the case of aluminum chloride, a mixture of $Al(NO_3)_3$ and $Al(NO_3)_3 \cdot N_2O_4$ is obtained. As indicated below, the latter compound is probably best formulated as $NO[Al(NO_3)_4]$.

In the presence of a small amount of water, lithium carbonate is solvolyzed in accordance with the equation:

$$Li_2CO_3 + 2N_2O_4 \rightarrow 2LiNO_3 + N_2O_3 + CO_2$$

Liquid dinitrogen tetroxide likewise reacts with calcium oxide, calcium carbonate, sodium carbonate, sodium hydroxide, zinc carbonate, and zinc sulfide to give anhydrous nitrates, sometimes admixed with nitrites. The reactions are, in many cases, quite slow and may sometimes be speeded up by adding small quantities of water. Commonly one can do this and still obtain an anhydrous nitrate product.

Reactions with Metals. Very active metals react with liquid dinitrogen tetroxide in a manner analogous to their reactions with water.

$$M_{(s)} + N_2O_{4(l)} \rightarrow NO + MNO_3 \text{ (M = alkali metal)}$$

$$M_{(s)} + H_2O_{(l)} \rightarrow \tfrac{1}{2}H_2 + MOH$$

Just as the addition of hydrogen chloride to water increases its reactivity toward metals so also the addition of NOCl to liquid dinitrogen tetroxide increases its reactivity toward metals. Thus, metals such as zinc, iron, and tin react with solutions of NOCl in liquid dinitrogen tetroxide as follows.

$$M_{(s)} + 2NOCl \xrightarrow[N_2O_4]{\text{liq.}} MCl_2 + 2NO \text{ (M = Zn, Fe, Sn, etc.)}$$

analogous to

$$M_{(s)} + 2HCl \xrightarrow{H_2O} MCl_2 + H_2$$

Amphoteric metals such as zinc behave toward liquid dinitrogen tetroxide solutions in a manner analogous to their behavior toward aqueous acids and bases. Thus, zinc metal reacts only very slowly with liquid dinitrogen tetroxide. However, zinc reacts rapidly with solutions of NOCl (see above) or $[Et_2NH_2]NO_3$ in this solvent.

$$Zn + x[Et_2NH_2]NO_3 + 2N_2O_{4(l)} \rightarrow$$

$$[Et_2NH_2]_x[Zn(NO_3)_{x+2}] + 2NO$$

Diethyl Ammonium Nitratozincate
(exact composition unknown)

analogous to

$$Zn + 2NaOH + 2H_2O \rightarrow Na_2[Zn(OH)_4] + H_2$$
$$Zn + 2KNH_2 + 2NH_3 \rightarrow K_2[Zn(NH_2)_4] + H_2$$

Zinc nitrate dissolves readily in solutions of diethyl ammonium nitrate in liquid dinitrogen tetroxide to yield a nitrato zinc complex.

$$Zn(NO_3)_{2(s)} + x\ [Et_2NH_2]NO_3 \xrightarrow[N_2O_4]{liq.} [Et_2NH_2]_x[Zn(NO_3)_{x+2}]$$

This reaction is analogous to the following:

$$Zn(OH)_{2(s)} + 2NaOH \xrightarrow{H_2O} Na_2[Zn(OH)_4]$$

$$Zn(NH_2)_{2(s)} + 2KNH_2 \xrightarrow[NH_3]{liq.} K_2[Zn(NH_2)_4]$$

$$Al_2(SO_3)_{3(s)} + 3(Me_4N)_2SO_3 \xrightarrow[SO_2]{liq.} 2[Me_4N]_3[Al(SO_3)_3]$$

Copper metal reacts with a solution of dinitrogen tetroxide in ethyl acetate to yield a compound having the formula $Cu(NO_3)_2 \cdot N_2O_4$. Zinc nitrate reacts with liquid dinitrogen tetroxide to give the solvate $Zn(NO_3)_2 \cdot 2N_2O_4$. Uranyl nitrate, $UO_2(NO_3)_2$, likewise forms the solvate $UO_2(NO_3)_2 \cdot N_2O_4$. The solvate $Fe(NO_3)_3 \cdot N_2O_4$ has also been prepared. These solvates may be formulated as the complex salts $NO[Cu(NO_3)_3]$, $(NO)_2[Zn(NO_3)_4]$, $NO[UO_2(NO_3)_3]$ and $NO[Fe(NO_3)_4]$.

Molecular Addition Compounds of Dinitrogen Tetroxide

Interesting as solvent system relationships may be, it is in the area of molecular addition compounds that much of the recent work in dinitrogen tetroxide chemistry has been done.

It is well known, for example, that the course of nitration reactions in which dinitrogen tetroxide is used as a nitrating agent may be strongly modified by the choice of solvent for the nitration reaction. In general, it was found that solvents which are strong electron donors give a distinctly different reaction than occurs in non-donor solvents. This led to speculation concerning the possible formation of addition compounds between dinitrogen tetroxide and Lewis bases.

During recent years many binary systems composed of dinitrogen tetroxide with a variety of electron-donor substances have been investigated. These investigations have involved, in most instances, the cryoscopic determination of the freezing point-composition curves for the systems (Figs. 4.1a,b,c,d,e,f). From the form of these curves the existence of various compounds can be detected.

Dinitrogen Tetroxide-Ether Systems. Binary systems of dinitrogen tetroxide with a variety of different ethers have been

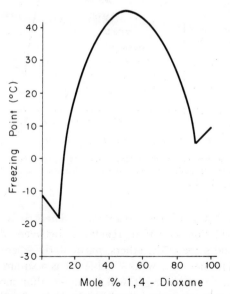

Fig. 4.1a. The freezing point diagram for the system N_2O_4 - 1,4-dioxane. Indicates formation of addition compound $N_2O_4 \cdot O(CH_2CH_2)_2O$.

studied. Most of these ethers form compounds which, because of their low melting points and the very flat maxima in their freezing point curves, are assumed to be of rather low stability. In general, there is a strong correlation between compound formation and the effect of the ether as a

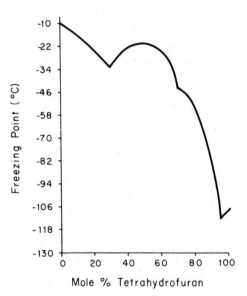

Fig. 4.1b. The freezing point diagram for the system N_2O_4 - tetrahydrofuran. Indicates formation of the addition compounds $N_2O_4 \cdot C_4H_8O$ and probably $N_2O_4 \cdot 2C_4H_8O$.

solvent for N_2O_4 nitration reactions. There is a tendency toward oxidation-reduction reactions between dinitrogen tetroxide and some of the ethers, particularly where addition compound formation is weak. Table 4.1 is a summary of the results of these studies. It will be noted that most of the compounds correspond to the formula $N_2O_4 \cdot 2R_2O$; several

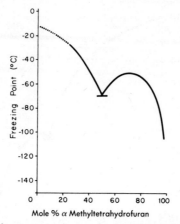

Fig. 4.1c. The freezing point diagram for the system N_2O_4-α-methyltetrahydrofuran. Indicates formation of addition compound $N_2O_4 \cdot 2C_4H_7(CH_3)O$.

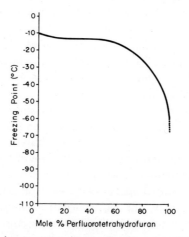

Fig. 4.1d. The freezing point diagram for the system N_2O_4 - perfluorotetrahydrofuran. No addition compound forms.

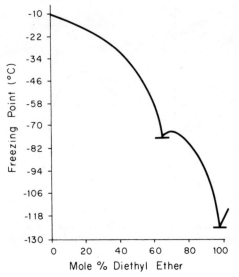

Fig. 4.1e. The freezing point diagram for the system N_2O_4 - diethyl ether. Indicates formation of addition compound $N_2O_4 \cdot 2(C_2H_5)_2O$.

ethers form, in addition, compounds of the formula $N_2O_4 \cdot R_2O$. The "dibasic" ethers, such as 1,4-dioxane and 1,3-dioxane, form 1 : 1 compounds, but these are equivalent to 1 : 2 compounds of "monobasic" ethers.

The failure of t-butyl ether to form an addition compound whereas n-butyl ether does form such a compound is best explained by steric interference of the bulky tertiary butyl groups with the ether oxygen. In the case of β,β'-dichlorodiethyl ether, the failure to form a compound with dinitrogen tetroxide may be attributed either to electron withdrawal from the ether oxygen by the electronegative chlorine atoms or steric interference of the bulky chlorine atoms or perhaps a combination of the two effects.

It is also interesting to compare tetrahydrofuran with perfluorotetrahydrofuran:

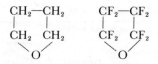

Perfluorotetrahydrofuran gives no evidence at all for compound formation with dinitrogen tetroxide. This is to be expected on the basis of the assumption that these N_2O_4-ether addition compounds result from Lewis acid-base interaction, for the electron-withdrawing effect of the fluorine atoms robs the ether oxygen of any electron-donor capacity.

Most striking, however, among these interactions, is the formation of the rather stable complexes of dinitrogen tetroxide with 1,4-dioxane, and to a slightly lesser degree with 1,3-dioxane. 1,4-Dioxane forms the white crystalline complex, $N_2O_4 \cdot O(CH_2CH_2)_2O$, which melts at $+45.2°C$, and, at room temperature, is a *white, crystalline, diamagnetic* solid. (Re-

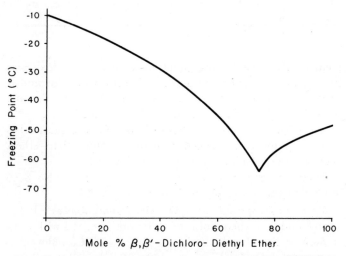

Fig. 4.1f. The freezing point diagram for the system N_2O_4 - β,β'-dichloro-diethyl ether. No addition compound forms.

TABLE 4.1.   Molecular Compounds of N_2O_4 With Ethers

Ether Used	Mole Ratio N_2O_4 : Ether in Compound	Melting Point of Compound	Stability of Compound at Melting Point
Ethyl ether	1 : 2	−74.8	low
n-Propyl ether	1 : 2(?)	−77.5(incong.)*	very low
i-Propyl ether	1 : 2(?)	−65.0(incong.)	very low
n-Butyl ether	1 : 2(?)	−79.5(incong.)	very low
t-Butyl ether	...	...	...
$(ClCH_2CH_2)_2O$	...	...	...
Trimethylene oxide	1 : 1	−53.5	low
	1 : 2	−53.4	low
Tetrahydrofuran	1 : 1	−20.5	moderate
	1 : 2(?)	−43.0(incong.)	...
Perfluorotetrahydrofuran	...	...	...
α-Methyltetrahydrofuran	1 : 2	−50.5	moderate
2,4-Dimethyltetrahydrofuran	1 : 2	−34.	low
Tetrahydropyran	1 : 2	−56.8	moderate
1,4-Dioxane	1 : 1	+45.2	stable
1,3-Dioxane	1 : 1	+ 2.0	moderate
Trioxane	1 : 1(?)	−11.0(incong.)	...
Ethyleneglycoldiethyl ether	1 : 1	ca. −60	very low
	1 : 2	ca. −60	very low

*incong. = incongruent melting point.

member that the boiling point of dinitrogen tetroxide is
21.3°C and, at this temperature, it is brown in color and is
definitely paramagnetic.)   The compound $N_2O_4 \cdot$ 1,3-dioxane
is similar in character although it melts at +2.0° C.

Binary Systems with Other Oxygen Bases. Cryoscopic studies
of systems involving oxygen compounds other than ethers
show a variety of addition compounds (Table 4.2).

Binary systems of some non-oxygen bases have also been
studied by the cryoscopic method (Table 4.3).

Molecular Compounds of N_2O_4 with Tertiary Amines. It has
been found that when dinitrogen tetroxide is mixed with tertiary amines in etheral solution at about −75° C, yellow pre-
cipitates of the general formula $N_2O_4 \cdot 2B$, where B is pyridine,

quinoline, isoquinoline, acridine, α-picoline, β-picoline, or tri-ethylamine, are formed. In contrast, the sterically hindered molecules 2,6-lutidine and 2-methylquinoline do not form addition compounds under these conditions.

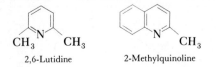

2,6-Lutidine 2-Methylquinoline

Addition products in which the mole ratio of N_2O_4 to B is considerably greater than 0.5 were also found when a considerable excess of dinitrogen tetroxide was used. The product ob-

TABLE 4.2. Molecular Compounds of N_2O_4 With Various Oxygen Bases

Oxygen Base	Mole Ratio N_2O_4 : Base in Compound	Melting Point of Compound °C	Stability of Compound (at Melting Point)
Sulfoxides			
$(CH_3)_2SO$	1 : 1	+38	stable
$(C_2H_5)_2SO$	1 : 1	+14	stable
$(n\text{-}C_3H_7)_2SO$	1 : 1	+20	stable
$(i\text{-}C_3H_7)_2SO$	1 : 1	−10	stable
Nitrosamines			
$(CH_3)_2NNO$	1 : 2	+ 3	moderate
$(C_2H_5)_2NNO$	1 : 2	−38	moderate
$(C_6H_5)(CH_3)NNO$	1 : 2 (?)	−17 (incong.)	
$(C_6H_5)(C_2H_5)NNO$	1 : 2	−12	mod. low
$CH_2 \overset{\displaystyle CH_2-CH_2}{\underset{\displaystyle CH_2-CH_2}{\diagdown}}NNO$	1 : 1	−33	moderate
	1 : 3	−18	moderate
Carbonyl Compounds			
$(C_6H_5)(CH_3)CO$	1 : 2 (?)	−11 (incong.)	
CH_3COOH	1 : 2	+ 2	moderate
$C_6H_5COOC_2H_5$	1 : 2	−13	moderate
$(CH_3)_2CO$	1 : 2	−40	moderate
C_6H_5CHO	1 : 1	−42	moderate

TABLE 4.3. Molecular Addition Compounds of N_2O_4 With Non-Oxygen Bases

Substance Studied	Mole Ratio N_2O_4 : Base in Compound	Melting Point of Compound °C	Stability of Compound (at Melting Point)
$C_6H_5CH_2CN$	1 : 2	−42	low
CH_3CN	1 : 1	−40	low
	1 : 2	−42	low
$ClCH_3CH_2CN$	1 : 2	−62	low
C_6H_5CN	1 : 1	−26	low
C_6H_6	1 : 1	− 7	moderate
$C_6H_3(CH_3)_3$ (Mesitylene)	1 : 1	−18	low
	1 : 1	−37	low
p-$C_6H_4(CH_3)_2$	no compd.	. . .	. . .
C_6H_{12}	no compd.	. . .	. . .
C_6H_5Cl	no compd.	. . .	. . .
C_6H_5Br	no compd.	. . .	. . .
$C_6H_5NO_2$*	1 : 1	−31	moderate

*The oxygen is not the basic center in this molecule.

tained with an excess of N_2O_4 on triethylamine is pink and highly explosive.

All of these products are unstable at room temperature, in fact at any temperature above 0° C, in some cases even lower.

Structures of Addition Compounds with Bases. Spectroscopic, magnetic, and chemical evidence indicates that binary systems composed of dinitrogen tetroxide and an electron donor involve the equilibrium (B = one molecule of the electron donor):

$$[(B)_nNO]^+[NO_3]^- \rightleftharpoons nB + N_2O_4 \rightleftharpoons N_2O_4 \cdot nB$$
$$\text{ionic} \qquad\qquad\qquad\qquad \text{molecular}$$

Where B is a very strong electron donor, the equilibrium will be shifted to the left and an ionic complex will be obtained.

Thus, it has been shown that the R_3N—N_2O_4 compounds are ionic, for solutions of N_2O_4 in R_3N are good electrical conductors. For very weak electron donors the equilibrium will be shifted to the right and molecular complexes will be formed.

On the basis of this concept the quite reasonable classification of dinitrogen tetroxide addition compounds expressed in Table 4.4 has been made.

TABLE 4.4. Addition Compounds of N_2O_4 With Bases

Donor	Liquid Phase	Solid Phase
Strong R_3N	ionic	ionic
Medium-Strength R_2O, R_2N—NO, RCN $R_2C{=}O, RC\overset{\overset{O}{\|}}{} {-}OR, R_2SO$	ionic $\rightleftharpoons$ molecular*	molecular
Weak $C_6H_6, C_6H_5NO_2$	molecular	molecular

*Generally only very small concentrations of the ionic form; principally molecular.

If we refer to the electronic formula for the N_2O_4 molecule presented above, it is apparent that by the process of breaking the π bonds in the N_2O_4 molecule, bonding orbitals on each of the nitrogen atoms may be made available for the acceptance of electron pairs from various donor molecules as indicated in the following diagram.

Since the coordination number of nitrogen atoms with respect to oxygen in nitric acid is limited to 3, it might be supposed that the acceptance of donor molecules by the nitrogen atoms in N_2O_4 might be sterically hindered. However, it will be recalled that the N—N distance in N_2O_4 is greater than normal and this would help to reduce the strain.

The ionic structure involves the sharing of electrons from the donor molecule with the nitrosylium ion, NO^+ This ion which contains only 10 valence electrons can upon saturation contain a total of 14 electrons. Thus, the NO^+ has the possibility of accepting either one of two electron pairs.

$$[B: \rightarrow \ddot{N}{=}\ddot{O}:^+][NO_3^-] \text{ or } \left[B: \rightarrow \underset{\overset{\uparrow}{\underset{.}{B}}}{\ddot{N}}{-}\ddot{O}:^+ \right] [NO_3^-]$$

Since the first of these structures would be favored, the distinctly ionic dinitrogen tetroxide compounds are chiefly 1 : 1 compounds.

The structure of the relatively stable and high-melting adduct of dinitrogen tetroxide with 1,4-dioxane has been postulated to be that presented below:

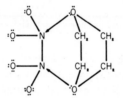

Compounds of Dinitrogen Tetroxide with Boron Trifluoride.
Boron trifluoride reacts with dinitrogen tetroxide in the gas phase, and in liquid sulfur dioxide to yield a white, crystalline compound with the composition expressed by the formula $N_2O_4 \cdot 2BF_3$. Magnetic, spectroscopic, X-ray, and chemical data indicate that this compound has the structure

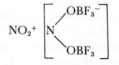

Evidence has been obtained for the formation of a white, crystalline solid having the composition $N_2O_4 \cdot BF_3$ with the probable structure

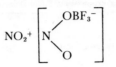

when boron trifluoride is added to an excess of dinitrogen tetroxide dissolved in a nitro-alkane solvent such as nitromethane or nitroethane. This adduct has proved useful as a nitration agent for organic compounds.

Summary of the Solvent Characteristics of Dinitrogen Tetroxide

Dinitrogen tetroxide is a solvent of very low dielectric constant but which behaves as an electron acceptor toward strong electron-donors, and acts as an electron donor toward strong electron-acceptors. Many molecular addition compounds have been reported. Nitrates behave as typical bases in this system and nitrosyl compounds are typical acids. Few ionic compounds are soluble in liquid dinitrogen tetroxide, but many covalent substances have high solubilities in this solvent. Because of its strong oxidizing character, liquid dinitrogen tetroxide is not compatible with many potential solutes.

B. CHEMISTRY IN LIQUID SULFUR DIOXIDE

Though sulfur dioxide is a gas under normal temperature and pressure, it is readily liquefied and is easily maintained in the liquid phase in ordinary Dewar type vessels. Its harmful physiological effects (breathing large quantities of the gas can be fatal and concentrations as low as 0.04% over an extended period of time can produce toxic symptoms) and its unpleasant odor dictate care in its use. Nevertheless, its interesting chemical properties combined with its low cost and ease of handling have resulted in considerable study of sulfur dioxide as a solvent for chemical reactions.

The principal physical properties for sulfur dioxide are summarized in Table 4.5.

TABLE 4.5.   Physical Properties of Sulfur Dioxide

Freezing point, °C	−75.46
Boiling point, °C	−10.02
Specific conductivity, ohm^{-1}cm^{-1}	4×10^{-8} (−10° C)
Density, g./ml.	1.46 (−10° C)
Viscosity, poise	0.004285 (−10° C)
Dielectric constant	15.6 (0° C)
Dipole moment, debyes	1.61
Vapor pressure, atmospheres	$\begin{cases} 1.530 \ (0° \text{C}) \\ 3.228 \ (20° \text{C}) \end{cases}$

Structure of the Sulfur Dioxide Molecule

The structure of the sulfur dioxide molecule in the gaseous state has been shown by electron diffraction to correspond to the following diagram:

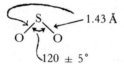

This structure may be rationalized as a resonance hybrid of the following structures:

Since by the opening up of the bond, as indicated in the following structure,

the sulfur atom is left with a vacent bonding orbital, it is not surprising that sulfur dioxide acts as an electron acceptor and forms molecular complexes with a variety of electron-donor molecules.

Solubilities in Liquid Sulfur Dioxide

As might be predicted from its dielectric constant, sulfur dioxide is a better solvent for covalently bonded substances than for ionic substances. Substances such as bromine, iodine monochloride, boron trichloride, phosphorus trichloride, arsenic trichloride, carbon disulfide, phosphorus oxychloride, and a variety of sulfuryl compounds (SO_2X_2) are completely miscible with liquid sulfur dioxide. Iodine monobromide, phosphorus tribromide, and the tetrachlorides of carbon, silicon, germanium, and tin are quite soluble in this solvent. With few exceptions, liquid sulfur dioxide is an excellent solvent for organic compounds. Among the exceptions are the alkanes which have only a limited solubility. Aromatic hydrocarbons and the alkenes have much higher solubilities in liquid sulfur dioxide than do the alkanes. Liquid sulfur dioxide is, because of this differing solvent action towards various hydrocarbons, of considerable utility in the refining of petroleum.

Among ionic substances the iodides are, in general, the most soluble in liquid sulfur dioxide. Many thiocyanates are likewise quite soluble. Just as is the case with liquid ammonia, the solubilities of the alkali metal halides decrease in the order $I^- > Br^- > Cl^-$. Metal sulfates, sulfides, oxides, and hydroxides are virtually insoluble. The solubilities of a variety of salts are summarized in Table 4.6.

Many of the more soluble salts form solvates in liquid sulfur dioxide and, in general, the solubilities of salts in liquid sulfur dioxide may be roughly correlated with tendency toward solvate formation, although there are a few exceptions. Typical examples of solvates in the sulfur dioxide system are listed in Table 4.7.

TABLE 4.6. Solubilities of Ionic Compounds in Liquid Sulfur Dioxide at 0°C. (millimoles solute/1000 g. solvent)

	I^-	Br^-	Cl^-	F^-	SCN^-	CN^-	ClO_4	CH_3COO^-	$SO_4^{=}$	$SO_3^{=}$	$CO_3^{=}$
Li^+	1490.0	6.0	2.82	23.0				3.48	1.55	1.37	
Na^+	1000.0	1.36	insol	6.9	80.5	3.67		8.90	insol.	1.58	
K^+	2490.0	40.0	5.5	3.1	502.0	2.62		0.61	insol.	1.27	0.214
Rb^+			27.2								
NH_4^+	580.0	6.0	1.67		6160.0		2.14	141.0	5.07	2.67	
Tl^+	1.81	0.60	0.292	insol.	0.915	0.522	0.43	285.0	0.417	4.96	
Ag^+	0.68	0.159	<0.07	insol.	0.845	1.42		1.02	insol.	insol.	
Be^{++}			5.8								
Mg^{++}	0.50	1.3	1.47								
Ba^{++}	18.15	insol.	insol.		insol.					insol.	
Zn^{++}	3.45		11.75		40.4			insol.			
Cd^{++}	1.17		insol.								
Hg^{++}	0.265	2.06	3.80		0.632	0.556		2.98	0.338		
Pb^{++}	0.195	0.328	0.69	2.16	0.371	0.386		2.46	insol.		
Co^{++}	12.2		1.00		insol.						
Ni^{++}	insol.		insol.								
Al^{+++}	5.64	0.60	v. sol.					0.08	insol.		
Sb^{+++}	0.26	21.8	575.0	0.56							
Bi^{+++}		3.44	0.60								insol.

TABLE 4.7. Typical Salt Solvates with Sulfur Dioxide

Formula	Temp. at which p_{SO_2} = 1 atm (°C)	Heat of Vaporization (kcal./mole)
$[(CH_3)_4N]_2SO_4 \cdot 6SO_2$	− 2.6	8.53
$NaI \cdot 4SO_2$	+ 5.	9.63
$KI \cdot 4SO_2$	+ 6.	9.67
$RbI \cdot 4SO_2$	+15.5	10.03
$CaI \cdot 4SO_2$	+17.	10.89
$KBr \cdot 4SO_2$	− 1.	8.38
$CaI_2 \cdot 4SO_2$	+33.	10.7
$SrI_2 \cdot 4SO_2$	+34.	10.74
$BaI_2 \cdot 4SO_2$	+12.5	9.91
$RbI \cdot 3SO_2$	+15.3	10.5
$[(CH_3)_4N]_2SO_4 \cdot 3SO_2$	+28.	11.7
$LiI \cdot 2SO_2$	− 1.	9.4
$NaI \cdot 2SO_2$	+15.	10.01
$SrI_2 \cdot 2SO_2$	+42.5	11.06
$BaI_2 \cdot 2SO_2$	+49.5	11.34
$[(CH_3)_4N]Br \cdot 2SO_2$	+16.	10.3
$[(CH_3)_4N]Cl \cdot 2SO_2$	+35.	10.6
$AlCl_3 \cdot 2SO_2$	+80.	14.
$KSCN \cdot SO_2$	+12.5	9.91
$[(CH_3)_4N]Br \cdot SO_2$	+41.	8.89
$[(CH_3)_4N]Cl \cdot SO_2$	+88.	11.1
$KSCN \cdot 0.5SO_2$	− 49.	11.3
$RbSCN \cdot 0.5SO_2$	+31.5	10.64
$CsSCN \cdot 0.5SO_2$	+19.	10.14
$Ca(SCN)_2 \cdot 0.5SO_2$	+34.	10.74

A number of molecular addition compounds of sulfur dioxide with various electron-donor molecules have been observed. Some of these are listed in Table 4.8.

Electrolytic Behavior of Solutions in Sulfur Dioxide

Numerous conductivity and ebullioscopic measurements have been made on sulfur dioxide solutions, and they show that, in general, these solutions are not as good electrical conductors as liquid ammonia solutions or aqueous solutions are. The sulfur dioxide solutions of alkali metal, am-

TABLE 4.8.   Molecular Addition Compounds with Sulfur Dioxide

With Amines:	*With Ethers (Cont.):*
Quinoline $\cdot$ SO_2	$O(CH_2CH_2)_2O \cdot 2SO_2$
$C_6H_5N(CH_3)_2 \cdot SO_2$	$C_6H_5OCH_3 \cdot SO_2$
$C_6H_5NH_2 \cdot SO_2$	
$(CH_3)_3N \cdot SO_2$	*With GrIV Halides:*
Pyridine $\cdot$ SO_2	$TiBr_4 \cdot 0.5SO_2$
α-Picoline $\cdot$ SO_2	$TiCl_4 \cdot 0.5SO_2$
β-Picoline $\cdot$ SO_2	$SnBr_4 \cdot 0.5SO_2$
γ-Picoline $\cdot$ SO_2	
With Ethers:	*Others:*
CH_2—$CH_2 \cdot SO_2$	$BF_3 \cdot SO_2$
$\diagdown _O \diagup$	$CH_3COOH \cdot SO_2$
	$(C_2H_5)_2S \cdot SO_2$
$O(CH_2CH_2)_2O \cdot SO_2$	

monium, and tetraalkylammonium chlorides, bromides, iodides, and thiocyanates are moderately good conductors but the mono-, di-, and trialkylammonium salts are very poor conductors. Since because of the relatively low dielectric constant of the solvent, interionic attraction is large in liquid sulfur dioxide, it is only at extremely low concentrations that solutions of electrolytes in liquid sulfur dioxide give conductivities corresponding to the limiting values calculated for the completely dissociated electrolyte.

The order of increasing dissociation and conductivity of electrolytes in liquid sulfur is roughly proportional to the size of the cation, the following order being observed: $Na^+ <$ $NH_4^+ < K^+ < Rb^+ < (CH_3)_3S^+ < (CH_3)_4N^+ < (C_2H_5)_4N^+ <$ $(CH_3C_6H_4)_3C^+$. In the case of salts of a common cation, the following order of conductivities for various anions has been observed: $SCN^- < ClO_4^- < Cl^- < Br^- < I^- < SbCl_6^-$. Thus, it is clear that other effects than anionic size operate in this series. Measurements of ion mobilities in liquid sulfur dioxide show the following sequences:

A. $(CH_3)_4N^+ < K^+ < NH_4^+ < Rb^+$
B. $SCN^- < Br^- < I^-$
C. $ClO_4^- < Cl^-$

A number of substances which are covalent in nature and which would not be expected to yield conducting solutions in liquid sulfur dioxide have been shown to behave as electrolytes in this solvent. Examples of such substances include Br_2, I_2, PBr_5, $AsBr_3$, $SbCl_5$, S_2Br_2, IBr, ICl, ICl_3, $(C_6H_5)_3CCl$,

$SOBr_2$, $(CH_3)_2CHC\overset{\displaystyle O}{\underset{\displaystyle Br}{\diagdown}}$, $CH_3OC_6H_4CCl_2C_6H_4OCH_3$, CH_3-

$OC_6H_4CHClCH{=}CClC_6H_4OCH_3$, $CH_3OC_6H_4CHClCH{=}$ $CClCH{=}CHC_6H_4OCH_3$.

In the case of triphenylchloromethane and certain of its chloro- and methyl derivatives, the conductance of solutions in liquid sulfur dioxide may be interpreted in terms of the following equilibria:

$$(C_6H_5)_3CCl \rightleftharpoons \underbrace{(C_6H_5)_3C^+Cl^-}_{\text{Ion Pair}} \rightleftharpoons (C_6H_5)_3C^+ + Cl^-$$

$$K = \frac{[(C_6H_5)_3C^+][Cl^-]}{[(C_6H_5)_3CCl] + \underbrace{[(C_6H_5)_3C^+Cl^-]}_{\text{Ion Pair}}}$$

Values of K for this equilibrium and the ionization equilibria of several substituted triphenylchloromethanes are listed in Table 4.9.

It is interesting to note that solutions of trisubstituted hydronium salts in liquid sulfur dioxide are moderately good

TABLE 4.9. Values for K at $0.175°C$

Solute	$K_{(moles/1.)}$	
$(C_6H_5)_3CCl$	4.15	$\times 10^{-5}$
$(o\text{-}ClC_6H_4)(C_6H_5)_2CCl$	1.06	$\times 10^{-5}$
$(m\text{-}ClC_6H_4)(C_6H_5)_2CCl$	0.153	$\times 10^{-5}$
$(p\text{-}ClC_6H_4)(C_6H_5)_2CCl$	1.26	$\times 10^{-5}$
$(p\text{-}ClC_6H_4)_3CCl$	0.122	$\times 10^{-5}$
$(o\text{-}CH_3C_6H_4)(C_6H_5)_2CCl$	62.5	$\times 10^{-5}$
$(m\text{-}CH_3C_6H_4)(C_6H_5)_2CCl$	9.5	$\times 10^{-5}$
$(p\text{-}CH_3C_6H_4)(C_6H_5)_2CCl$	77.	$\times 10^{-5}$

electrical conductors. Examples include $[(C_2H_5)_3O]BF_4$, $[(CH_3)_3O]BF_4$, and $[(C_2H_5)_3O]SbCl_6$, all of which have electrical conductivities in liquid sulfur dioxide of the same order of magnitude as do solutions of potassium iodide of similar concentrations. In this same connection, it should be noted that whereas neither water nor hydrogen bromide by itself yields an electrically conducting solution in sulfur dioxide, a mixture of water and hydrogen bromide dissolves in liquid sulfur dioxide to give a conducting solution. Electrolysis of this solution results in the liberation of water and hydrogen at the cathode and of bromine at the anode. Furthermore, the ratio of the amounts of water liberated to the quantity of electricity passed through the solution corresponds to that calculated on the basis of the equation:

$$H_3O^+ + e^- \longrightarrow H_2O + \tfrac{1}{2} H_2$$

Somewhat less than the theoretical quantity of hydrogen is liberated; however, this may have resulted from the secondary reduction of another species, possibly sulfur dioxide itself, by the liberated hydrogen. These experiments support, in general, the postulate of the existence of the hydronium ion formed by the reaction of water with hydrogen bromide.

$$H_2O + HBr \longrightarrow H_3O^+ + Br^-$$

Reactions in Liquid Sulfur Dioxide

Autoionization and Acid-Base Reactions. The electrical conductivity of pure liquid sulfur dioxide (4×10^{-8} ohm^{-1}cm^{-1} at $-10.°C$) is commonly interpreted* in terms of self-ionization in accordance with the following equation:

$$2SO_2 \rightleftharpoons SO^{++} + SO_3^=$$

which may be considered as analogous to the corresponding self-ionization reactions for water and liquid ammonia:

*Jander, G. and Wickert, K., *Z. physik. Chem.* **A178,** 57 (1936).

$$2H_2O \rightleftharpoons H_3O^+ + OH^-$$

$$2NH_3 \rightleftharpoons NH_4^+ + NH_2^-$$

According to this formal analogy, the SO^{++} ion would be the analogue of the hydronium and ammonium ions, and the sulfite ion, $SO_3^=$, would be analogous to the hydroxide and amide ions.

Thus, typical bases in the sulfur dioxide systems would include those compounds which contain or make available sulfite ion. Thus, the alkali metal sulfites should behave as typical bases in liquid sulfur dioxide. The actual species present is probably the pyrosulfite ion, $S_2O_5^=$, formed by the solvation reaction

$$SO_3^= + SO_2 \rightarrow S_2O_5^=$$

In the reactions which follow we shall write it as simply sulfite, $SO_3^=$.

Similarly, it would be expected that compounds which contain or make available the SO^{++} ion would be typical acids in liquid sulfur dioxide. Thus, thionyl compounds, such as $SOCl_2$ or $SOBr_2$, would behave as acids. It is not necessary that these thionyl compounds be actually appreciably ionized into SO^{++} ions but only that they are capable of reacting in such a way as to make this ion available in a chemical reaction.

Several typical acid-base reactions which have been carried out in liquid sulfur dioxide include the following:

$$Cs_2SO_3 + SOCl_2 \rightarrow 2CsCl + 2SO_2$$

$$K_2SO_3 + SO(SCN)_2 \rightarrow 2KSCN + 2SO_2$$

$$[(CH_3)_4N]_2SO_3 + SOBr_2 \rightarrow 2[(CH_3)_4N]Br + 2SO_2$$

Whereas, in analogy with reactions between bases and acids in aqueous solution, it is tempting to assume that the reactions between sulfites and thionyl compounds in sulfur dioxide occur by ionic mechanisms and may be represented by the equation

$$SO_3^= + SO^{++} \rightleftharpoons 2SO_2$$

it is not necessary to make this assumption. In fact, studies[*] of the kinetics of exchange of radioisotopes of sulfur between thionyl halides and sulfur dioxide, as well as between tetra-methylammonium pyrosulfite and sulfur dioxide, make it quite clear that the free ion SO^{++} plays no important role in the mechanism of reactions in liquid sulfur dioxide. Mechanisms involving the transfer of $O^=$ ions have been suggested for the explanation of acid-base phenomena in liquid sulfur dioxide.

Experimental evidence supports the partial ionization of thionyl halides as, for example, the following equation indicates:

$$SOCl_2 \overset{SO_2}{\rightleftharpoons} SOCl^+ + Cl^-$$

Solvolytic Reactions. Solvolytic reactions of salts in liquid sulfur dioxide are much less common and are generally more complex than is true of solvolytic processes in many protonic solvents. Examples of such reactions include the reaction of zinc diethyl with sulfur dioxide at Dry Ice temperatures,

$$Zn(C_2H_5)_2 + 2SO_{2(l)} \rightarrow ZnSO_3 + (C_2H_5)_2SO$$

(analogous to $Zn(C_2H_5)_2 + 2H_2O \rightarrow Zn(OH)_2 + 2C_2H_6$)

the solvolysis of ammonium acetate,

$$2NH_4(O{-}\overset{\overset{\displaystyle O}{\|}}{C}{-}CH_3) + 2SO_2 \rightarrow (NH_4)_2SO_3 + (CH_3\overset{\overset{\displaystyle O}{\|}}{C}{-}O)_2SO$$

$$\Updownarrow$$

$$SO_2 + (CH_3\overset{\overset{\displaystyle O}{\|}}{C}{-})_2O$$

[*]Johnson, R., Norris, T., and Huston, J., *J. Am. Chem. Soc.*, **73**, 3052 (1951).

(analogous to $NH_4(O-\overset{\overset{\displaystyle O}{\|}}{C}-CH_3) + H_2O \rightarrow NH_4OH +$

$HO\overset{\overset{\displaystyle O}{\|}}{C}CH_3)$

and the following reactions of sulfur dioxide with binary halides:

$$PCl_5 + SO_{2(l)} \rightarrow POCl_3 + SOCl_2$$

$$PBr_5 + SO_{2(l)} \rightarrow POBr_3 + SOBr_2$$

$$NbCl_5 + SO_{2(l)} \xrightarrow{70°C} NbOCl_3 + SOCl_2$$

$$WCl_6 + SO_{2(l)} \xrightarrow{70°C} WOCl_4 + SOCl_2$$

$$2UCl_5 \xrightarrow{90°C} UCl_6 + UCl_4$$
$$UCl_6 + 2SO_2 \rightarrow UO_2Cl_2 + 2SOCl_2$$

Numerous other halides, such as $SbCl_3$, $SbCl_5$, $SiCl_4$, $SnCl_4$, VCl_5, SCl_2, SCl_4, and $MoCl_6$, have been shown to be unaffected by liquid sulfur dioxide.

Alkali metal halides react slowly with liquid sulfur dioxide, but the reactions are complex and alkali metal sulfates sometimes mixed with other substances are obtained. The course of the reaction in the case of potassium bromide is presumed to be as follows:

$$8KBr + 8SO_2 \rightarrow 4K_2SO_3 + 4SOBr_2$$
$$4SOBr_2 \rightarrow 2SO_2 + S_2Br_2 + 3Br_2$$
$$\underline{4K_2SO_3 + 2Br_2 \rightarrow 2K_2SO_4 + 4KBr + 2SO_2}$$
$$4KBr + 4SO_2 \rightarrow 2K_2SO_4 + S_2Br_2 + Br_2$$

It may be noted that the first step in the above mechanism is analogous to hydrolytic and ammonolytic reactions:

$$MX + H_2O \rightarrow MOH + HX$$
$$MX + NH_3 \rightarrow MNH_2 + HX$$

and the formation of sulfate and other products results from secondary reactions.

Amphoterism in Liquid Sulfur Dioxide. Several reactions have been observed in liquid sulfur dioxide which are analogous to the behavior of amphoteric hydroxides in aqueous systems. For example, the treatment of aluminum chloride in sulfur dioxide solution with tetramethylammonium sulfite results in the formation of a gelatinous precipitate of aluminum sulfite.

$$2AlCl_3 + 3[(CH_3)_4N]_2SO_3 \rightarrow Al_2(SO_3)_{3(s)} + 6[(CH_3)_4N]Cl$$

This reaction is analogous to

$$AlCl_3 + 3NaOH \rightarrow Al(OH)_{3(s)} + 3NaCl$$

If the aluminum sulfite precipitate is rapidly treated with an excess of the ammonium sulfite, the precipitate redissolves just as aluminum hydroxide dissolves in an excess of sodium hydroxide solution.

$$Al_2(SO_3)_{3(s)} + 3[(CH_3)_4N]_2SO_3 \rightarrow 2[(CH_3)_4N]_3[Al(SO_3)_3]$$

$$Al(OH)_3 + NaOH \rightarrow Na[Al(OH)_4]$$

Further, if the acid $SOCl_2$ is added to the resulting solution, the aluminum sulfite reprecipitates, just as the addition of stoichiometric amounts of hydrochloric acid to the aqueous sodium hydroxy-aluminate solution results in the reprecipitation of aluminum hydroxide.

$$2[(CH_3)_4N]_3[Al(SO_3)_3] + 3SOCl_2 \rightarrow 6[(CH_3)_4N]Cl + 6SO_2 + Al_2(SO_3)_3$$

$$Na[Al(OH)_4] + HCl \rightarrow NaCl + H_2O + Al(OH)_3$$

Excess thionyl chloride does not redissolve the aluminum sulfite, however. Metals whose hydroxides are amphoteric generally dissolve in aqueous alkali solutions with the liberation of hydrogen. Most of these metals, however, including beryllium, aluminum, gallium, antimony, and lead, do not react with sulfur dioxide solutions of tetramethylammonium sulfite. Tin foil reacts with an excess of tetramethylammonium sulfite dissolved in sulfur dioxide in accordance with the following sequence of equations:

$$Sn + [(CH_3)_4N]_2SO_3 + 4SO_2 \rightarrow [(CH_3)_4N]_2Sn(SO_3)_3 + 2SO$$

$$2SO \rightarrow SO_2 + S$$

$$[(CH_3)_4N]_2SO_3 + S \rightarrow [(CH_3)_4N]_2S_2O_3$$

Complex Formation. Studies of reactions in sulfur dioxide solution have furnished a number of examples of complex ion formations. The solubility of iodine in liquid sulfur dioxide is greatly increased by the addition of potassium or rubidium iodide; the conductance of the latter is also increased by the addition of iodine.

$$RbI \text{ (or KI)} + I_2 \xrightarrow{SO_2} RbI_3 \text{ (or KI}_3)$$

Similarly, the solubilities of cadmium or mercuric iodides in sulfur dioxide are increased by the presence of potassium or rubidium iodide, thus indicating that complexes are formed. Other examples of complex formation involving antimony compounds are represented by the following equations:

$$SbCl_3 + 3KCl \xrightarrow{SO_2} K_3[SbCl_6]$$

$$SbCl_5 + KCl \xrightarrow{SO_2} K[SbCl_6]$$

$$2SbCl_3 + 3SOCl_2 \xrightarrow{SO_2} (SO)_3[SbCl_6]$$

$$[(CH_3)_4N]Cl + SbCl_5 \xrightarrow{SO_2} [(CH_3)_4N][SbCl_6]$$

$$NOCl + SbCl_5 \xrightarrow{SO_2} NO[SbCl_6]$$

$$CH_3C\overset{\displaystyle O}{\underset{\displaystyle Cl}{\big\langle}} + SbCl_5 \xrightarrow{SO_2} [CH_3C\overset{\displaystyle O}{=}][SbCl_6]$$

Another interesting example of complex formation is the reaction of boron trifluoride with acetyl fluoride in sulfur dioxide.

$$CH_3C\!\!\begin{array}{c}O\\ \diagup\\ \diagdown\\ F\end{array} + BF_3 \xrightarrow{SO_2} [CH_3C\!\!\begin{array}{c}O\\ \diagup\\ \diagdown\end{array}][BF_4]$$

Reactions with Organic Compounds. Because of the considerable solubility of organic compounds in liquid sulfur dioxide, and because of the non-inflammability and relative inertness toward organic compounds of this solvent, as well as its convenient temperature range, liquid sulfur dioxide is a useful solvent for several types of organic synthetic reactions. Among these is the sulfonation of aromatic hydrocarbons by chlorosulfuric acid or sulfur trioxide.

$$C_6H_6 + SO_3 \xrightarrow{SO_2} C_6H_5SO_3H$$

$$C_6H_6 + ClSO_3H \xrightarrow{SO_2} C_6H_5SO_3H + HCl$$

Yields from such sulfonation reactions in sulfur dioxide are good.

Sulfur dioxide is also an excellent solvent for Friedel-Crafts type reactions. Aluminum chloride, commonly used as a catalyst for Friedel-Crafts reactions, has a high solubility in liquid sulfur dioxide. Examples of such reactions which have been carried out in liquid sulfur dioxide include, among others, the following:

$$C_6H_6 + t\text{-}C_5H_{11}Cl \xrightarrow[SO_2]{AlCl_3} t\text{-}C_5H_{11}C_6H_5 + HCl$$

$$C_6H_6 + C_6H_5C\!\!\begin{array}{c}O\\ \diagup\\ \diagdown\\ Cl\end{array} \xrightarrow[SO_2]{AlCl_3} C_6H_5C\!\!\begin{array}{c}O\\ \diagup\diagdown\end{array}\!\!-C_6H_5 + HCl$$

$$C_6H_5OH + C_6H_5\overset{\displaystyle O}{\underset{\displaystyle Cl}{C}} \xrightarrow[SO_2]{AlCl_3} C_6H_5O-\overset{\displaystyle O}{C}-C_6H_5 + HCl$$

Sulfur dioxide has also served as a solvent for both the addition of bromine to unsaturated compounds, as well as for substitution reactions involving elementary bromine. Thus, both of the following reactions occur almost quantitatively in liquid sulfur dioxide.

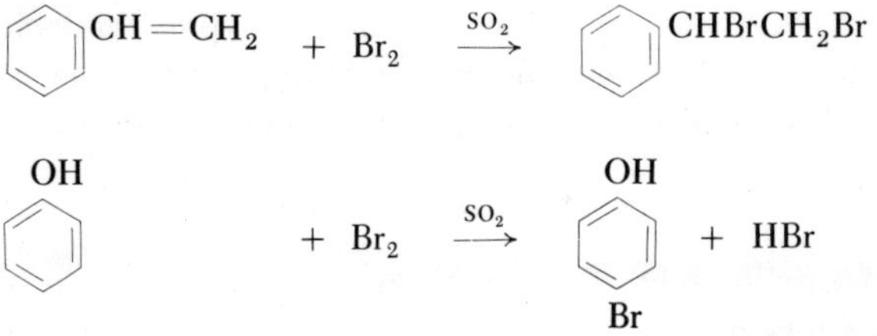

Metatheses which Depend on Solubility. As in the other solvents we have discussed, there are precipitation reactions which may be most conveniently carried out in liquid sulfur dioxide because of the specific solubility relationships which characterize that particular solvent. A few examples of such reactions are:

$$2Ag(O\overset{\displaystyle O}{\overset{\displaystyle \|}{C}}CH_3) + SOCl_2 \xrightarrow{SO_2} 2AgCl_{(s)} + SO(O\overset{\displaystyle O}{\overset{\displaystyle \|}{C}}-CH_3)_2$$

$$2KBr + SOCl_2 \xrightarrow{SO_2} 2KCl_{(s)} + SOBr_2$$

$$2NH_4SCN + SOCl_2 \xrightarrow{SO_2} 2NH_4Cl_{(s)} + SO(SCN)_2$$

$$2KI + SOCl_2 \xrightarrow{SO_2} 2KCl_{(s)} + SOI_2$$

Thionyl iodide, thionyl thiocyanate, and thionyl acetate have not been isolated from the mother liquor of these reactions, presumably because of secondary decomposition reactions which occur.

Summary of the Solvent Characteristics of Liquid Sulfur Dioxide

Sulfur dioxide is a solvent of intermediate dielectric constant in which a number of ionic compounds have a limited solubility and a few ionic compounds have a large solubility. Many covalent compounds are highly soluble in liquid sulfur dioxide. Sulfur dioxide is a strong electron-acceptor and forms molecular complexes with many electron donors. Sulfites (M_2SO_3) (or pyrosulfites) behave as typical bases in this solvent, and thionyl compounds (SOX_2) behave as typical acids. It is doubtful, however, that the ionic reaction

$$SO^{++} + SO_3^= \rightleftharpoons 2SO_2$$

plays a major role in the mechanisms of acid-base reactions in this solvent. Sulfur dioxide is a useful solvent for several types of synthetic reactions and in the refining of certain types of petroleum.

Selected Readings

A. DINITROGEN TETROXIDE
1. Addison, C. C., and Hathaway, B. J., "Addition Compounds of Dinitrogen Tetroxide and Their Application in Preparative Inorganic Chemistry," pp. 33–44 of "Recent Aspects of the Inorganic Chemistry of Nitrogen," Special Publication No. 10 of The Chemical Society (London) 1957.
2. Gray, P., "The Chemistry of Dinitrogen Tetroxide. Monograph No. 4," The Royal Institute of Chemistry, London, 1958.
3. Sisler, H. H. *J. Chem. Educ.*, **34**, 555–561 (1957).

B. SULFUR DIOXIDE
1. Audrieth, L. I., & Kleinberg, J., "Non-Aqueous Solvents," Chap. 2, John Wiley & Sons, Inc., New York, 1953.
2. Jander, G., "Die Chemie in Wasserähnlichen Lösungsmitteln," Chap. 8, Springer-Verlag, Berlin, 1949.

THE SCOPE OF
NON-AQUEOUS SOLVENT
CHEMISTRY

WE HAVE IN THIS discussion of chemistry in non-aqueous solvents accomplished the following objectives: (1) we have examined various aspects of the role that the solvent plays in determining the chemistry characterizing systems in which the particular solvent is the reaction medium; and (2) we have examined in some detail the specific chemistries associated with four familiar non-aqueous solvent systems. These particular systems were chosen because they exemplify four radically different sets of solvent properties.

We shall conclude with a short discussion which will give some indication of the great variety of solvents at the disposal of the chemist, and mention a few pertinent facts concerning some of these.

Basic Solvents

In addition to liquid ammonia, there are a variety of other compounds which have suitable properties to make them useful as basic solvents. Included among this group of compounds are the following substances which have received some attention as solvents: the simple primary amines, particularly methylamine and ethylamine; polyamines, such as ethylenediamine; hydroxy-amines, such as the ethanolamines $HOCH_2$-CH_2NH_2, $(HOCH_2CH_2)_2NH$, and $(HOCH_2CH_2)_3N$; heterocyclic, aromatic bases, notably pyridine; and hydrazine and its organic derivatives. As might be predicted, the solubilities of ionic compounds in the organic nitrogen bases tend to be less than in liquid ammonia. However, many ionic substances are appreciably soluble in pyridine. This probably results from the strong tendency for pyridine to form coordination compounds with various electron acceptors. A list of salts which are soluble in pyridine is given in Table 5.1.

TABLE 5.1.   Solubilities in Pyridine*

Soluble Salts:

LiCl, LiBr, LiI, $LiNO_3$, NaBr, NaI, NaSCN, $NaNO_2$; KCN, KSCN, $KMnO_4$; NH_4SCN; CuCl, CuBr, CuSCN, CuF_2; AgSCN, $AgNO_2$, $AgNO_3$, $AgC_2H_3O_2$, Ag_2SO_4; $BeCl_2$; $MgCl_2$, $MgBr_2$, MgI_2; $Ca(NO_3)_2$, $CaCl_2$, $CaBr_2$, CaI_2; $SrCl_2$, SrI_2; $BaCl_2$, BaI_2; $ZnCl_2$, $ZnBr_2$, $Zn(CN)_2$, $Zn(SCN)_2$; CdI_2, $Cd(SCN)_2$; $HgCl_2$, $HgBr_2$, HgI_2, $Hg(CN)_2$, K_2HgI_4; $AlBr_3$; $SnCl_2$, $SnBr_2$, $SnCl_4$; $Pb(SCN)_2$, $PbCl_2$, $Pb(NO_3)_2$, $Pb(C_2H_3O_2)_2$; TiF_4; $CrCl_2$, CrO_3; $MnCl_2$; $FeCl_2$, $FeCl_3$, $PtCl_4$; $LaCl_3$; $CeCl_3$, $CeBr_3$; UBr_4, UO_2Cl_2, UO_2I_2, $UO_2(NO_3)_2$.

Insoluble Salts:

LiOH; NaOH; KOH, KNO_3, KCl, KBr, KI; NH_4Cl, NH_4I; CuCN, $Cu(NO_3)_2$; $BaBr_2$, $Ba(NO_3)_2$; $CdCl_2$, $CdBr_2$, $Cd(NO_3)_2$; $Hg(NO_3)_2$; $AlCl_3$; $PbBr_2$, PbI_2; $SbCl_3$; $BiCl_3$; $CrCl_3$; $Co(NO_3)_2$; $Ni(NO_3)_2$. Hg(I) salts; Rb salts; Cs salts; M^+ or M^{++} borates, carbonates, silicates, phosphates, arsenates, sulfides, sulfites, and chromates; Li^+, Na^+, and K^+ chlorates, perchlorates, bromates and iodates.

*Naumann, *Ber.*, **37**, 4609 (1904); Schroeder, *Z. anorg. Chem.*, **44**, 1 (1905); Nelson, *J. Am. Chem. Soc.*, **35**, 658 (1913).

Though the primary aliphatic amines and ethylenediamines are poorer solvents than liquid ammonia, these substances are qualitatively similar to liquid ammonia in their solvent characterics.

Hydrazine. Hydrazine, NH_2NH_2, is an interesting potential solvent because of its high dielectric constant (51.7 at 25°C, which makes it a good solvent for ionic substances), its basic character (slightly less than that of ammonia), and its convenient liquid range ($20°C$ to $113.5°C$). Disadvantages include a strong tendency to absorb carbon dioxide and water vapor and a tendency to undergo reaction with molecular oxygen, a reaction which is strongly catalyzed by such metals as copper. Because of the strong reducing character of hydrazine, many solutes are reduced when dissolved in this solvent. For example, many salts of the less active metals are reduced to the free metals upon solution in hydrazine.

Hydrazine may be considered formally to be the parent solvent for a hydrazine system of acids, bases, and salts. This formal relationship is illustrated in Table 5.2 in which a few analogous members of the water, ammonia, and hydrazine series are listed.

TABLE 5.2. Analogous Compounds in the Water, Ammonia, and Hydrazine Systems

Water System	*Ammonia System*	*Hydrazine System*
$NaOH$	$NaNH_2$	$NaNHNH_2$
H_3O^+	NH_4^+	$NH_2NH_3^+$
ROH	RNH_2	$RNHNH_2$
$R_2C{=}O$	$R_2C{=}NH$	$R_2C{=}NNH_2$
$CO(OH)_2$	$C(NH)(NH_2)_2$	$C(NNH_2)(NHNH_2)_2$

(R = an organic group or hydrogen)

The strongest acid capable of existence in hydrazine solution is the hydrazinium ion $NH_2NH_3^+$ and the strongest base available in this medium is the hydrazide ion $NHNH_2^-$. A typical neutralization reaction in this system is the reaction between hydrazinium chloride and potassium hydrazide.

$$NH_2NH_3^+, Cl^- + K^+, NHNH_2^- \rightarrow 2NH_2NH_2 + K^+, Cl^-$$

or simply

$$NH_2NH_3^+ + NHNH_2^- \rightarrow 2NH_2NH_2$$

As in water and ammonia, many substances undergo solvolysis in hydrazine. Examples of such solvolytic processes include the following:

$$RC\!\!\stackrel{O}{\diagup}\!\!OR' + NH_2NH_2 \rightarrow RC\!\!\stackrel{O}{\diagup}\!\!NHNH_2 + R'OH$$

$$RC\!\!\stackrel{O}{\diagup}\!\!Cl + 2NH_2NH_2 \rightarrow RC\!\!\stackrel{O}{\diagup}\!\!NHNH_2 + NH_2NH_3{}^+, Cl^-$$

$$Na^+, FSO_3{}^- + 2NH_2NH_2 \rightarrow Na^+, SO_3NHNH_2{}^- + NH_2NH_3{}^+, F^-$$

$$C_5H_5N:SO_3 + 2NH_2NH_2 \rightarrow C_5H_5N + NH_2NH_3{}^+, SO_3NHNH_2{}^-$$

Physical constants for several basic solvents are listed in Table 5.3.

Neutral Solvents

The organic chemist has made available a great variety of solvents which do not differ greatly from water in basicity or acidity but which have distinctly different solvent characteristics. Among these are the many alcohols, the ethers, the glycols, the esters, and the alkyl sulfoxides among the oxygen compounds. Diethers such as "Diglyme," the dimethyl ether of ethylene glycol, are important solvents. Nitrogen-containing members of this class include nitriles such as acetonitrile, nitralkanes such as nitromethane, and acid amides such as formamide and its N-substituted derivatives. Formamide and dimethyl formamide are very important additions to the chemist's arsenal of solvents, for because of their organic nature and high dielectric constants (formamide, 109 (20°C); dimethyl formamide, 26.6 (25°C)) these two substances combine high solvent power toward ionic compounds with considerable ability to dissolve organic compounds. Acetonitrile (dielectric constant 36 at 20°C) is likewise an excellent solvent for many ionic substances. This solvent forms a variety of complexes with various metal salts.

TABLE 5.3. Physical Constants of Some Non-Aqueous Solvents

Solvent	Dielectric Constant	M.P. (°C)	B.P. (°C)	Specific Conductivity (ohm⁻¹cm⁻¹)	Viscosity (centipoise)	Density (g./cc.)
Methylamine	$\cdots$	-93.5	-6.3	9×10^{-8}	$\cdots$	0.699 (-11°C)
Ethylenediamine	12.9 (25°C)	11.0	116.2		1.725 (25°C)	0.891 (25°C)
Hydrazine	51.7 (25°C)	2.	113.5	2.3 to 2.6 $\times 10^{-6}$ (25°C)	0.905 (25°C)	1.011 (15°C)
Pyridine	12.5 (20°C)	-40.7	115.5	$<1 \times 10^{-9}$	0.945 (20°C)	1.00304 (0°C)
Ethyl alcohol	24.3 (25°C)	-114.5	78.4	1.35×10^{-9} (25°C)	$\cdots$	0.789 (20°C)
Diethyl ether	4.34 (20°C)	-116.3 (α) -123.3 (β)	34.6	$<4 \times 10^{-13}$ (25°C)	0.2448 (20°C)	0.708 (25°C)
Acetonitrile	37.5 (20°C)	-44.9	81.6	7×10^{-6} (20°C)	$\cdots$	0.783 (20°C)
Nitromethane	35.87 (30°C)	-28.6	101.3	6×10^{-7} (18°C)	$\cdots$	1.131 (25°C)
Formamide	109. (20°C)	2.6	193.	4×10^{-6} (25°C)	0.659 (120°C)	1.133 (20°C)
Dimethyl formamide	26.6 (25°C)	-61.	153.	$\cdots$	0.802 (25°C)	0.9445 (25°C)
Dimethyl sulfoxide	45.	18.45	189.	$\cdots$	1.1 (27°C)	1.100 (20°C)
Acetic acid	6.15 (20°C)	16.6	118.1	0.5×10^{-8} (25°C)	1.222 (20°C)	1.049 (20°C)
Hydrogen cyanide	114.9 (20°C)	-13.35	25.7	5×10^{-7} (0°C)	0.201 (20.2°C)	0.688 (20°C)
Hydrogen fluoride	84. (0°C)	-83.	19.4	1.4×10^{-5}	0.240 (6.25°C)	0.988 (13.64°C)

Physical constants for several neutral solvents are listed in Table 5.3.

Acidic Solvents

In addition to 100% sulfuric acid which we discussed in detail in Chapter Three, several other acids have been studied as solvents for chemical reactions. Notable among these are anhydrous acetic acid, hydrogen cyanide, and hydrogen fluoride.

Acetic Acid. Acetic acid is an interesting acidic solvent which has some very unusual characteristics. Its physical constants are listed in Table 5.3. Measurements of the dipole moment of acetic acid indicate a value of zero. This is most surprising in view of the unsymmetrical structure of the acetic acid molecule.

This apparent anomaly is explained by the fact that acetic acid molecules are united by hydrogen bonds to form dimers with the following symmetrical structure in which the electric moments of the two molecules cancel:

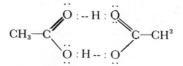

It appears that certain solutes can promote the dissociation of these dimers and the formation of solvates of the respective solutes by solvate-solute interaction involving, in many instances, hydrogen bonding between solute and solvent molecules. Other solvents are not capable of this. This leads to uncertainty in predicting behavior in this solvent. In general, the low dielectric constant of acetic acid precludes the existence of highly dissociated ionic species in this medium. Thus, salts which in water behave as strong electrolytes exist in acetic acid principally in the form of neutral aggregates of positive and negative ions, probably ion pairs. This effect, in addition to the relatively low proton affinity (basicity) of acetic acid, results in strong acids such as perchloric having relatively small ionization constants in this solvent.

$$HClO_4 + CH_3C\!\!\begin{array}{c}O\\ \diagup\\ \diagdown\\ OH\end{array} \rightleftharpoons CH_3C(OH)_2^+ + ClO_4^-$$

$$K_{ion} = 9 \times 10^{-7}$$

Thus, the leveling effect of acetic acid toward various acids (p. 8) is much less than the leveling effect of water toward acids. Acids such as perchloric, hydrobromic, sulfuric, hydrochloric, and nitric, which appear to be of equal strength in aqueous solution, are readily differentiated by comparing the conductivities of their acetic acid solutions. The order of acid strength thus established is

$$HClO_4 > HBr > H_2SO_4^* > HCl > HNO_3 \longrightarrow$$

The strongest acid available in acetic acid is the acetonium ion, $CH_3C(OH)_2^+$. Since acetonium ion is a much stronger acid than hydronium ion, H_3O^+, acetic acid is very useful for carrying out chemical reactions requiring stronger acids than hydronium ion, and which, therefore, may not be carried out in water.

The leveling effect of acetic acid toward bases is very strong, all strong bases being solvolyzed to acetate ion, which is the strongest base capable of existence in acetic acid solution.

*First step in the dissociation only.

A typical neutralization reaction in acetic acid solution is represented by the following equation:

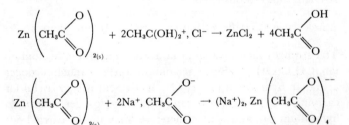

$$CH_3C(OH)_2^+, ClO_4^- + Na^+, CH_3C\overset{O^-}{\underset{O}{}} \rightarrow$$

$$Na^+, ClO_4^- + 2CH_3C\overset{OH}{\underset{O}{}}$$

or simply

$$CH_3C(OH)_2^+ + CH_3C\overset{O^-}{\underset{O}{}} \rightarrow 2CH_3C\overset{OH}{\underset{O}{}}$$

Amphoteric behavior in the acetic acid system is exemplified by zinc acetate which is only very slightly soluble in acetic acid, but which dissolves in acetic acid solutions of hydrogen chloride or acetic acid solutions of sodium acetate.

$$Zn\left(CH_3C\overset{O}{\underset{O}{}}\right)_{2(s)} + 2CH_3C(OH)_2^+, Cl^- \rightarrow ZnCl_2 + 4CH_3C\overset{OH}{\underset{O}{}}$$

$$Zn\left(CH_3C\overset{O}{\underset{O}{}}\right)_{2(s)} + 2Na^+, CH_3C\overset{O^-}{\underset{O}{}} \rightarrow (Na^+)_2, Zn\left(CH_3C\overset{O}{\underset{O}{}}\right)_4^{--}$$

These reactions are analogous to the reactions of zinc hydroxide with hydrochloric acid and sodium hydroxide in the aqueous system.

Solubilities of various salts in acetic acid are indicated in Table 5.4.

TABLE 5.4. Solubilities of Salts in Acetic Acid*

Insoluble:
> AgCl, AgBr, AgI, AgCN, AgSCN, PbCl$_2$, PbI$_2$, Hg$_2$Cl$_2$, CdI$_2$, Ba(NO$_3$)$_2$,
> Ca$_3$(PO$_4$)$_2$, CaCO$_3$, Cu$_3$(PO$_4$)$_2$, Fe(C$_2$H$_3$O$_2$)$_3$, most sulfates

Solubility less than 1%:
> NaCl, NaNO$_3$, Na$_2$SO$_4$, KCl, KBr, KI, KNO$_3$, KClO$_3$, NH$_4$Cl, NH$_4$Br,
> NH$_4$I, (NH$_4$)$_2$SO$_4$, BaCl$_2$, Zn(CH$_3$COO)$_2$, Ca(CH$_3$COO)$_2$, Ag(CH$_3$COO)

Sparingly soluble:
> AgNO$_3$, AlCl$_3$, CoCl$_2$, HgCl$_2$, HgI$_2$, Cu(CH$_3$COO)$_2$

Readily soluble:
> LiNO$_3$, Li(CH$_3$COO), Na(CH$_3$COO), KCN, K(CH$_3$COO), NH$_4$NO$_3$,
> NH$_4$SCN, NH$_4$(CH$_3$COO), Ca(NO$_3$)$_2$, CaCl$_2$, Cu(NO$_3$)$_2$, ZnCl$_2$, FeCl$_3$,
> SbCl$_3$, BaI$_2$, Ba(CH$_3$COO)$_2$, ZnI$_2$, Pb(CH$_3$COO)$_2$, Cd(CH$_3$COO)$_2$
> Sr(CH$_3$COO)$_2$, Tl(CH$_3$COO)

*Davidson, *J. Am. Chem. Soc.*, **50,** 1890(1928); Davidson and McAllister, *J. Am. Chem. Soc.*, **52,** 507(1930).

Acetic acid is an excellent solvent for organic compounds and is widely used in organic synthetic procedures which require an acidic solvent.

Hydrogen Cyanide. Liquid hydrogen cyanide is a weakly acidic solvent which has a surprisingly high dielectric constant (123 at 15.6°C). Many ionic compounds dissolve in this solvent. Its tendency to form solvates is not very great, however, and its solvent power for ionic compounds is inferior to that of water. It is an excellent solvent for organic compounds. Its physical constants are listed in Table 5.3.

Hydrogen Fluoride. Liquid hydrogen fluoride is a strongly acidic solvent which, as indicated by its relatively high specific conductivity, has a relatively high degree of autoionization.

$$2HF \rightleftharpoons H_2F^+ + F^-$$

Some important physical constants for liquid hydrogen fluoride are given in Table 5.3.

Because of the high acidity of the solvent, most anions are sufficiently basic to react directly with the solvent

$$X^- + HF \rightarrow HX + F^-$$

and anions other than fluoride are usually present in only limited concentrations.

The strongest acid available in the solvent is the ion H_2F^+, which is a strong acid indeed. Few substances are sufficiently acidic to donate a proton to hydrogen fluoride to form this ion. The few which are capable of this include fluoboric acid (HBF_4), fluophosphoric acid (HPF_6), fluoarsenic acid ($HAsF_6$), and fluoantimonic acid ($HSbF_6$). Of these the last is the strongest. The strongest base available in liquid hydrogen fluoride is fluoride ion, which is a relatively weak base.

Solubilities of a series of inorganic compounds are summarized in Table 5.5.

TABLE 5.5. Solubilities in Liquid Hydrogen Fluoride

Highly soluble:
  NH_4F, LiF, NaF, KF, RbF, CsF, TlF, AgF, $NaNO_3$, KNO_3, $AgNO_3$, $NaSO_4$, K_2SO_4, Ag_2SO_4, Tl_2SO_4, $NaC_2H_3O_2$, $KC_2H_3O_2$, $(NH_4)_2S_2O_8$, $K_2S_2O_8$, H_2O

Slightly soluble:
  CO, CO_2, H_2S, $CaSO_4$, MgF_2, CaF_2, SrF_2, BaF_2

Not appreciably soluble:
  HCl, HBr, HI, $Cu(NO_3)_2$, $Bi(NO_3)_3$, $Pb(NO_3)_2$, $Co(NO_3)_2$, $ZnSO_4$, $CuSO_4$, $CdSO_4$, CuF_2, ZnF_2, PbF_2, AlF_3, FeF_3, SiF_4

Undergo solvolysis to yield a soluble product:
  Alkali chlorides, alkali bromides, alkali iodides, alkaline earth chlorides, alkaline earth bromides, alkaline earth iodides, KCN, NaN_3, K_2SiF_6, $KClO_3$, Ag_2O, $K_2Cr_2O_7$, $KMnO_4$

Unreactive and insoluble:
  HgO, PbO_2, MnO_2, SnO_2, Cr_2O_3, WO_3, Mn_2O_3, AgCl, AgBr, AgI, CuCl, $CuCl_2$, $ZnCl_2$; $CdCl_2$, $HgCl_2$, HgI_2, $SnCl_2$, $ZnCl_2$

React to give insoluble product:
  $AlCl_3$, $FeCl_2$, $MnCl_2$, $CeCl_3$, MgO, CaO, BaO, BaO_2, CuO

Liquid hydrogen fluoride is an exceptionally good solvent for most organic compounds. This is usually related to the organic compound acting as a base toward hydrogen fluoride.

Hydrogen fluoride has had wide use both in research and in industry as a solvent for a variety of synthetic reactions, particularly in systems requiring a highly acidic medium. Examples of such reactions include the nitration and sulfonation of aromatic hydrocarbons, the fluorination of organic compounds by electrolysis of their solutions in liquid hydrogen fluoride, fluorination of organic compounds with elementary fluorine in liquid hydrogen fluoride, as well as a series of molecular rearrangements which are catalyzed by hydrogen fluoride.

Acid Halides

A number of acid halides have been studied as solvents for chemical reactions, but these have not been widely used. Some properties of a few of these solvents are listed in Table 5.6.

Halogens and Interhalogens

Illustrating the fact that for special purposes some very unusual solvents may be used is the investigation of the free halogens and the interhalogen compounds as solvents. Iodine and bromine trifluoride have received considerable attention in this connection. Iodine is notable for its ability to dissolve alkali metal iodides, and bromine trifluoride has proved particularly useful for the synthesis of a number of complex fluorides difficult to prepare in the usual solvents. Physical constants and auto-ionization equilibria for iodine and some of the interhalogens are listed in Table 5.7.

Fused Salts

We have omitted entirely any specific reference to solvent systems capable of being used at higher temperatures. Such systems include fused salts, fused oxide melts, and fused metals. The fields of metallurgy and ceramics are specifically concerned with such high-temperature solvent systems. Though the phenomena encountered in these systems may be somewhat strange, they are susceptible to explanation by the same set of principles which we have used in considering the

TABLE 5.6. Physical Constants for Some Acid Halide Solvents

Solvent	Postulated Self-Ionization	Dielectric Constant	M.P. (°C)	B.P. (°C)	Specific Conductivity (ohm⁻¹cm⁻¹)	Density (g./cc.)
$SeOCl_2$	$2SeOCl_2 \rightleftharpoons$ $(SeOCl \cdot SeOCl_2)^+ + Cl^-$	46.2 ± 1 (20°C)	10.8	177.6	2.0×10^{-5} (25°C)	2.44 (22°C)
$COCl_2$	$COCl_2 \rightleftharpoons COCl^+ + Cl^-$	4.34 (22°C)	−104.	8.2	7×10^{-9} (25°C)	1.392 (19°C)
$NOCl$	$NOCl \rightleftharpoons NO^+ + Cl^-$	18.2 (12°C)	−64.5	−5.5	2.88×10^{-6} (−20°C)	1.417 (−12°C)
$POCl_3$	$POCl_3 \rightleftharpoons POCl_2^+ + Cl^-$	13.9 (22°C)	1.25	105.8 (753 mm)	1.71×10^{-6} (25°C)	1.675 (25°C)

TABLE 5.7. Physical Constants for Iodine and Some Interhalogens

Solvent	Postulated Auto-ionization	Dielectric Constant	M.P. (°C)	B.P. (°C)	Specific Conductivity (ohm⁻¹cm⁻¹)	Viscosity (centipoise)	Density (g./cc.)
I_2	$2I_2 \rightleftharpoons I^+ + I_3^-$	11.08 (118°C)	113.6	184.35	$.9 \times 10^{-5}$— 1.7×10^{-4} (140°C)	1.414 (b.p.)	3.918 (133.5°C)
BrF_3	$2BrF_3 \rightleftharpoons BrF_2^+ + BrF_4^-$	42.6 (142°C)	8.8	127.6	8.0×10^{-3} (25°C)	...	2.843 (8.8°C)
ICl	$2ICl \rightleftharpoons I^+ + ICl_2^-$		27.2 (α) 13.9 (β)	97	4.42×10^{-3} (27.2°C)	4.19 (28.4°C)	3.13 (45°C)
IBr	$2IBr \rightleftharpoons I^+ + IBr_2^-$		42	ca 116	4.0×10^{-4} (42°C)	...	3.7616 (42°C)
IF_5	$2IF_5 \rightleftharpoons IF_4^+ + IF_6^-$	97.6 (120°C)	9.6	98	2×10^{-5} (25°C)	...	3.33 (9.6°C)

various non-aqueous solvents discussed in this brief monograph.

Conclusion

In this small book we have only briefly sampled the phenomena associated with the effects which solvents exert on the courses of chemical reactions. This should have sufficed, however, to demonstrate that unless chemical reactions occur in the gaseous phase, it is necessary, in order to understand the reactions, to consider the media in which the various reactants are suspended; and that by varying these media we can greatly alter the nature of the reaction.

Selected Readings

1. Audrieth, L. F., and Kleinberg, J., "Non-Aqueous Solvents," Chaps. 7, 8, 10, 12, 13, and 14, John Siley & Sons., Inc., New York, 1953.
2. Jander, G., "Die Chemie in Wasserähnlichen Lösungsmitteln," Chaps. 2, 5, 6, and 7, Springer-Verlag, Berlin, 1949.
3. Sneed, M. C., and Brasted, R. C., "Comprehensive Inorganic Chemistry," Vol. 5, Chap. 3 (by A. R. Pray), D. Van Nostrand Co., Inc., Princeton, N. J., 1956.

INDEX